This illustrated study manual on Romans continues the new Bible self-study series on personal, firsthand Bible study.

Each lesson of the manual is arranged so as to encourage you to make an independent analysis of the Bible text before referring to outside aids. Comments on selected portions of the passage are given at the end of the lesson. At that point in your study you will find it profitable to refer to more extensive outside sources (e.g., see Bibliography), for answers to questions raised in the course of your analysis.

Introduction   Outlines of the whole book of Romans and of its parts are given in chart form throughout this manual. This video method of outlining is used throughout the present Bible study series by the writer. One of the main advantages of such a method of outlining is that various outlines of the same Bible portion may be viewed and compared simultaneously.

The steps of Bible study of any one passage are these: observation, interpretation, application. You first must see what the Bible text says (observation) in order to interpret what it means (interpretation). Whenever observation questions are given in this manual without a related interpretive question, you should arrive at answers to such interpretive questions as:

1. What does it mean?
2. What does it imply?
3. What is its significance?

...possible, apply the text to everyday life.

...of classes:

1. *Length of study units.* There are fourteen lessons in this manual, but it is not necessary that a full lesson be studied at each class meeting. Sometimes, because of the large content of a passage being studied, two or more class meetings may be devoted to one lesson. You as leader of the class should decide before the following meeting how much of the lesson is to be studied. Do not try to hurry or crowd the class discussions. It pays to make haste *slowly* in the study of the book of Romans.

2. *Homework.* Urge each member of the class to complete the analysis suggestions of the manual before coming to class. This includes writing out answers whenever possible. It is important that each member think and study for himself, so that he can more accurately weigh what someone else says about a Bible text. Encourage the class to write down questions that arise in the course of study, and to bring them to the class hour for discussion. Don't ever embarrass a person by underestimating the significance of a question asked, regardless of its type. It is a healthy sign of mental activity when questions are asked; and Bible teaching is more pertinent in an environment of asking questions.

3. *Reading all Bible references.* Be sure to have all Scripture references looked up and read. This should not be neglected. The confirmation and illumination which is thrown on a passage of Scripture by other passages, is beyond estimation. The best commentary on the Bible is the Bible itself. Christians should get in the habit of comparing scripture with scripture. This may involve immediate context or distant context. In both instances the references are necessary for accurate Bible interpretation.

4. *Survey outlines.* It is important for the class to have a mental picture of the whole book of Romans while studying any part of it. Therefore Chart D and other shorter charts should be thoroughly studied and frequently referred to. The divisions of the epistle should be accurately learned and memorized. It would be well to have this chart enlarged on a blackboard or on paper and kept before the class at each meeting for reference and review.

5. *Use of modern Bible versions.* Analytical Bible study should *concentrate* on one version of the Bible, and *com-*

pare readings of other versions. The basic version referred to in this self-study series is the Authorized Version (King James). Highly recommended versions for Bible analysis are the American Standard Version (1901) and the New American Standard Bible (N.T., 1964). Encourage the class members to refer to at least one modern version of Romans as they analyze the Bible text in their basic version. Such a comparative study throws light on obscure passages, extends the scope of vision, and excites overall interest in the passage being studied. A recommended parallel-column edition of New Testament versions is The Four Translation New Testament, containing these versions: King James, New American Standard Bible, Williams, and Beck. In the foreword of this edition is this pertinent remark: "The beauty of the King James must be supplemented with the clarity of modern language. Perhaps the most effective way to retain the beauty and inspiration of one translation while benefiting from the clarity of another is to study the two together."*

6. *The class hour.* Devote most of the time to class discussion of the Bible text. Avoid the straight lecture approach. Encourage participation in discussion by *all* members. At the beginning of the lesson, review the main parts of the previous lesson. At the close of the discussion, emphasize especially the practical application of the truths learned.

* * *

The darkness of the world today—politically, socially, morally, religiously—is not the invention of a pessimist. It is real and tragic, a condition brought about by the sinfulness of man.

If there is any hope, it does not originate in man. It must come from a righteous, all-powerful and loving God.

The gospel message is God's good news to all people that there is hope, based on faith in Jesus Christ as Saviour and Lord. This was the message which Paul was inspired to write down in Romans, the book of our present study.

°The Four Translation New Testament, p. vi.

Publisher's Note

Enlarged charts related to the lessons of this study guide are available in *Jensen's Bible Study Charts* (Chicago: Moody, 1981). They were originally published in three volumes (Vol. 1, General Survey; Vol. 2, Old Testament; Vol. 3, New Testament).

The 8½ x 11" charts are especially valuable for Bible study groups, and can be reproduced as Xerox copies or as transparencies for overhead projectors. Selected transparencies are included.

Introduction
to Paul's Epistles

THE WRITINGS OF PAUL—AT LEAST

13 OF 21 EPISTLES—CONSTITUTE

A MAJOR PART OF THE NEW TESTAMENT.

A fourteenth book, Hebrews, also may have been written by Paul. All twenty-seven New Testament books are shown in Chart A.

GENERAL OUTLINE OF THE NEW TESTAMENT   Chart A

Nine of Paul's letters are addressed to seven Gentile churches (in Rome, Corinth, Galatia, Ephesus, Philippi, Colosse and Thessalonica). Locate these places on a map.

°These were written during Paul's first Roman imprisonment. Second Timothy, Paul's "dying letter," was written during his second imprisonment.

Four of Paul's letters are addressed to individuals (Timothy, Titus and Philemon). The epistle to the Hebrews was written especially for Jewish Christians and may have been intended as a circular letter.

The epistles of Paul are not listed chronologically in the New Testament canon. Chart B is an outline of highlights of Paul's life and indicates a probable chronological order of their writing.[†]

OUTLINE OF HIGHLIGHTS OF PAUL'S LIFE   Chart B

Birth of Paul	around the time of Christ's birth
Conversion of Paul	A.D. 33
First missionary journey	47-48
GALATIANS written after first journey[‡]	48
Apostolic council at Jerusalem	49
Second missionary journey	49-52
I and II THESSALONIANS written during second journey	52
Third missionary journey	52-56
I and II CORINTHIANS written during third journey	55
ROMANS written during third journey	56
Arrest in Jerusalem	56
Journey to Rome	60-61
In Rome awaiting trial, under guard	61
PHILEMON, COLOSSIANS, EPHESIANS, PHILIPPIANS written from prison	61
Paul released, revisits churches, resumes evangelistic ministry	62-66
I TIMOTHY, TITUS written	62-65
Paul arrested, imprisoned at Rome	66-67
II TIMOTHY written from prison	67
Paul executed	67

The order in which Paul's epistles are listed in the New Testament canon is generally topical, as shown below. Basically there are two main groups: epistles addressed to local churches (Rom. to II Thess.), and epistles addressed to individuals (I Tim. to Philemon). Within each group the epistles are arranged in descending order of length.[§]

[†]Some dates shown can only be approximated.

[‡]Some hold that Galatians was not written until a later date, for example after the third missionary journey, around A.D. 56.

[§]There is one minor exception to this order since Galatians is slightly shorter than Ephesians.

I. EPISTLES TO CHURCHES.

These epistles teach the proper order of the church and her relationship to Christ the Head. They also instruct the church as to her position, possessions, privileges and duties.

Romans has naturally the first place in order, since it is the foundational epistle of the doctrines of salvation. Romans shows the material out of which God forms the church: man lost in sin, hopeless, helpless. It also shows how God by His mighty power transforms this unpromising material into living stones of which the church is built, Christ Himself being the chief cornerstone.

Romans
I and II Corinthians
Galatians
Ephesians
Philippians
Colossians
I and II Thessalonians

II. EPISTLES TO INDIVIDUALS.

The message of these epistles applies especially to individual Christians, concerning Christian living and service:

I and II Timothy
Titus
Philemon

The Pauline Epistles were written by a special apostle (not one of the twelve), to a special body of people (the church), with a special object in view (the instruction of that body).

III. THE CHURCH IN THE NEW TESTAMENT.

Broadly speaking, the group of people which is the main object of attention in the New Testament is the church. The Gospels present Christ the foundation and Head of the church. The book of Acts records the beginning and early history of the church. The Epistles contain instructions for the church, and the book of Revelation prophesies concerning the church.

It is important to have clearly in mind just what the church is and who comprises it. Read I Corinthians 10:32 and note the reference to three groups: Jews, Gentiles and the church of God. Chart C identifies these in the stream of the human race.||

THE STREAM OF THE HUMAN RACE   Chart C

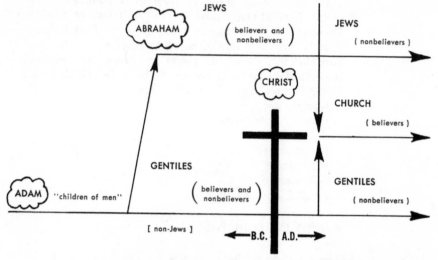

In the early generations of the human race there were no group distinctions, such as Jew and Gentile. All the descendants of Adam were as one family, "children of men," and God spoke to the whole race, seeking to get all people to obey Him and fellowship with Him. The race as a whole refused to do this, although there were some individuals who responded acceptably. Men persisted in doing their own will rather than God's will, and became utterly rebellious and disobedient. God allowed men to go on in their self-chosen ways.

But from the multitudes of the world living around 2000 B.C. God selected one man of faith, Abraham. From him He made a nation which was to be His chosen people, special representatives to whom and through whom He could speak and act. The top line of Chart C represents the descendants of Abraham, known as Jews or Israelites.

|| If Chart C included events of the last days, it would recognize Paul's prophecy of the rebirth of Israel (cf. Rom. 11:26).

8

The name Gentiles shown on the bottom line represents all other people.

Not all Jews were believers, just as not all Gentiles were unbelievers. For nearly two thousand years God patiently dealt with this chosen nation of Israel, seeking to get more than just a remnant to obey and represent Him. But the nation as a whole repeatedly refused to do this, although there were individual Israelites who obeyed. The nation became so corrupt and rebellious that God allowed them to go on in their self-chosen ways. The pattern was the same as for the human race before the time of Abraham.

Finally the day came when God sent His only begotten Son into the world, to redeem lost sinners (whether Jew or Gentile) and form a new unique people, the church. Not long after Christ's death, resurrection and ascension, the Holy Spirit came down from heaven to indwell and empower all members of that church. The church is now God's representative body of people on earth through whom He speaks to nonbelieving Jews and nonbelieving Gentiles (see Chart C). The true church of God is composed of all twice-born men, women and children, who have received a divine nature from God upon believing on Jesus Christ as their Saviour.

IV. THE MAIN PURPOSES OF THE EPISTLES.

All the New Testament Epistles—Pauline and General— complement the historical books of the Gospels and Acts by furnishing explanation and exhortation. The Gospels emphasize especially the facts of Christ's redemptive ministry; the Epistles interpret those facts and tell the redeemed ones how to live the Christian life. In the Gospels Christ announces His purpose to build the church (Matt. 16:16-18). Acts shows the church in the first stages of construction. The Epistles show how the church is built, what materials are used, and what are the position, relationships, privileges and duties of the members of its glorious and mysterious fellowship.

Prominent in all Paul's epistles are the exhortations and commands based on the doctrines. Seemingly simple duties are based on sublime truths originating with the person and work of Christ. Difficult commands (e.g., "present your bodies a living sacrifice," Rom. 12:1) are justified as being reasonable and consistent. Paul's epistles make it very clear that God offers all the help needed to fulfill His commands.

Every Christian should make a thorough study of Paul's epistles because of the tremendous truths which they reveal. Such truths must be clearly apprehended before we can enter into our full rights, privileges and powers as children and representatives of God. They are truths without which we cannot live or work as God would have us. It is because Paul so fully understood and entered into these truths that he had such marvelous power and success; and, just in proportion as we fail to apprehend and apply these truths contained in the epistles, will there be weakness, failure and misdirected effort in our lives.

In these epistles are revealed a number of vital truths about ourselves as Christians, any one of which, if fully understood and apprehended, would humble us to the dust or lift us to the gates of heaven. Be sure to read the verses cited in this list:

1. What we were: lost sinners under condemnation of death; children of the devil, helpless in the power of the great enemy of our souls (Rom. 1-3).

2. Who we are now: children of God; heirs of God and joint heirs with Jesus Christ (Rom. 8:16-17).

3. What we are: the temple of God; the dwelling place of the eternal Maker of the universe (I Cor. 3:16).

4. Where we are: in the heavenlies seated together with Christ (Eph. 2:6). "We live up there but we stay down here."

5. What we have: all things (Eph. 1:3; Rom. 8:32; I Cor. 3:21-22).

6. How we are to behave: walk worthy of our vocation (Eph. 4:1); worthy of the Lord (Col. 1:10); worthy of God (I Thess. 2:12).

7. Who our enemies are: Satan and all his hosts (Eph. 6:11-12).

8. How we are to meet our enemies: put on the whole armor of God (Eph. 6:10-11).

9. Where we are going: to be with Christ (I Thess. 4:17).

10. How we are to get there: no commonplace way (I Thess. 4:16-18).

11. What we are going to be like: like Christ (Eph. 4:13).
12. When this is to take place: when He shall appear (I Cor. 15:51-55; I Thess. 4:16).

Little did Paul and the other writers of New Testament Epistles realize the impact which their letters would make on the lives of people for two thousand years. One church historian has evaluated the Epistles thus:

> The Epistles of the New Testament are without a parallel in ancient literature . . . . Tracts for the times, they are tracts for all times. Children of the fleeting moment, they contain truths of infinite moment. They compress more ideas in fewer words than any other writings, human or divine, excepting the Gospels. They discuss the highest themes which can challenge an immortal mind—God, Christ, and the Spirit, sin and redemption, incarnation, atonement, regeneration, repentance, faith and good works, holy living and dying . . . . And all this before humble little societies of poor, uncultured artisans, freedmen and slaves!#

Review questions:

1. Which epistles of Paul were addressed to churches?

_____

_____

2. Which of his epistles were addressed to individuals?

_____

_____

3. Recall the approximate time and setting of the writing

of each of his epistles. _____

_____

_____

4. Account for the order in which Paul's epistles are listed

in the New Testament canon. _____

_____

#Philip Schaff, *History of the Christian Church* I, 740-41.

5. Contentwise, why is it appropriate that Romans stands first in the list of all the New Testament Epistles? _____

_____

6. What are the differences between Jew, Gentile and the church? _____

_____

_____

7. What main purposes do Paul's epistles serve in the New Testament? _____

_____

_____

8. What are some of the important truths taught by his epistles? _____

_____

_____

_____

LESSON 2

Background and Survey of Romans

ROMANS IS PAUL'S MASTERPIECE,

A KEY THAT UNLOCKS THE DOOR

TO VAST TREASURES OF SCRIPTURE.

People who have read and studied this epistle cannot find words sufficient to describe its worth. "The most profound book in existence" (Coleridge). "Cathedral of the Christian faith" (Godet). "The chief part of the New Testament and the very purest Gospel" (Luther). "A thorough study of this epistle is really a theological education in itself" (Griffith Thomas).

The uniqueness of Romans is not for telling a different gospel or a new teaching, but for spelling out the ABC's of the gospel of salvation in Christ, in clear, full fashion, so that there can be no question as to any important aspect of that gospel. Romans tells, for example, how sinful man can be restored to fellowship with his Creator, the holy God. It was of divine design that one epistle should be written especially to explain such truths to people, interpreting the truths already spoken by Jesus. Paul was the man chosen to be the writer, and Romans was the epistle. And under the guidance of the Holy Spirit this longest of the Epistles has been placed by the people of God first in the order of the New Testament Epistles.

Our study of Romans will follow the order which is recommended for any book study: first, introduction to the background of the book; then, survey of the book as a whole; then, analysis of each individual segment. Background and survey make up this lesson; analysis begins with Lesson 3.

I. BACKGROUND.

A. Author.

Paul was the author. Note the three ways Paul identifies himself in Romans 1:1. In your own words write down what is involved in each identification. Most of what is known about Paul's life is given to us in the book of Acts. It is recommended that Acts be studied as preparation for the study of any of Paul's epistles.

B. To Whom Written.

The letter was addressed to the saints in Rome (Rom. 1:7), a mixed group of Jews and Gentiles, the latter group probably constituting the majority (cf. 1:13; 2:17). These Christians had migrated to Rome from various parts of the Mediterranean world. Some no doubt were converts of Paul's and Peter's itinerant ministries. It is possible also that included in the number were "sojourners from Rome" (Acts 2:10, ASV) who had been present at Jerusalem on the day of Pentecost, and had returned to Rome with the message of Christ. Paul had not as yet visited this church at Rome when he wrote the epistle.

C. Date Written.

Paul wrote Romans from Corinth toward the end of his third missionary journey, around A.D. 56.

D. Occasion and Purpose of Writing.

Paul had various things in mind in writing this letter. Among them was his desire to tell the Roman Christians of his plan to visit them and to enlist their support of his proposed tour to Spain (15:23-25). The letter would also pave the way for Paul's personal visit by giving instruction to the Christians regarding the basic truths of salvation and Christian living. This intent of setting forth a comprehensive interpretation of the gospel must be the underlying purpose of the epistle, and almost two thousand years of church history have demonstrated successful fulfillment of such a divine purpose.

II. SURVEY.

As you begin your study of the actual text of Romans, decide on a version which you will use for the major part of your study. It is wise to concentrate one's study in one version, using other versions mainly for the sake of comparison and clarification. (The version used by this study guide is the Authorized or King James Version.)

A. Structure.

Read through the book of Romans in one sitting if possible, not slowly, seeking only in this survey to see such highlights as repeated words and subjects, groups of material and changes of subject. It is important that for this first reading you do not tarry over the text as though you were analyzing it. Otherwise the weight of sixteen chapters will suddenly bear down heavily upon you, and you will be discouraged from pursuing your study. It is true that profitable Bible study is work, but it need never be burdensome or uninteresting, if the study is pursued properly, prayerfully and with the guidance of the Holy Spirit. For this cursory reading it is recommended that you use a modern paraphrase of Romans, such as Living Letters or Phillips' Letters to Young Churches.

Next, observe the verse references of each segment shown on the survey Chart D. Note that all segments begin with the first verse of each chapter, with these exceptions: 1:18; 2:17; 3:9; 3:21; 9:30; 12:9; 15:14. Mark these segment divisions in the Bible version which you will be using as the basic text of your study. Then scan through Romans segment by segment, recording a segment title on Chart D. Note: A segment title should contain one to three words taken from the text, serving as a clue (not necessarily an outline) to the contents of the segment. See the two examples on Chart D.

The next step in survey study is to look for groups of segments according to content, and any turning point in the book. Do not refer to the outlines on chart D until you have first tried to arrive at your own outlines. Even if you do not arrive at a complete outline for the book, the time spent here in independent study is well spent, for you will begin to get acquainted more intimately with *what* Paul was writing as you try to discover *how* he wrote those truths. This is the search for *structure*, or organization of the book.

Record your outlines on a horizontal survey chart, and then compare your studies with the Chart D.

ROMANS   GOD'S SALVATION FOR SINNERS

Chart D

	PROLOGUE	DOCTRINAL					PRACTICAL	EPILOGUE
			SIN	SALVATION	SANCTIFICATION	SOVEREIGNTY	SERVICE	SERVICE BY FAITH

Gospel 1:1

PROLOGUE	DOCTRINAL				PRACTICAL	EPILOGUE
Salutation	God's Holiness in Condemning Sin	God's Grace in Justifying Sinners	God's Power In Sanctifying Believers	God's Sovereignty In Saving Jew and Gentile	God's Glory the Object of Service	Personal Notes
Personal Testimony					Consecration of Christians 12:1-2	
Theme Introduced					Practical Christian Service	Benediction and Doxology
					Glory of God 15:8-13	

Verse markers: 1:18, 2:1, 2:17, 3:9, 3:21, 4:1, 5:1, 6:1, 7:1, 8:1, 9:1, 9:30, 11:1, 12:1, 12:9, 13:1, 14:1, 15:14, 16:1

SIN	SALVATION	SANCTIFICATION	SOVEREIGNTY	SERVICE
slave to sin		slave to God		slave serving God

God's righteousness IN LAW	God's righteousness IMPUTED	God's righteousness OBEYED	God's righteousness IN ELECTION	God's righteousness DISPLAYED

LIFE BY FAITH				SERVICE BY FAITH
The Need of Salvation	The Way of Salvation	The Life of Salvation	The Scope of Salvation	The Service of Salvation
Deadliness of Sin	Design of Grace	power given	Demonstrations of Salvation promises fulfilled	paths pursued

KEY WORDS:
law, righteousness, faith, believe, sin, death, flesh, all, in Christ, Spirit.

KEY VERSES:
1:16-17

(handwritten notes): heart was darkened · Man w/o Excuse · All Under Sin

Observe the following with reference to survey Chart D:

1. Romans has sixteen chapters, broken down into 20 segments. The first segment (1:1-17) is the prologue, or introduction; the last two segments (15:14-33; 16:1-27) comprise the epilogue or conclusion.

2. The first eleven chapters are mainly *doctrinal*. In these chapters Paul presents the great truths of the gospel. The remaining chapters, 12-16, are mainly *practical*. In these chapters Paul shows the practical working out of the doctrines taught in chapters 1-11. Read Philippians 2:12-13 for what Paul has to say about working out one's salvation.

3. There is an ascending progression of subject in chapters 1-11, shown by the arrow. The progression moves from the wrath of God (God's Holiness in Condemning Sin) to the glory of God (God's Glory the Object of Service). Study the other parts of the outline as they fit into this progression. Note also from the outline of 12:1—15:13 what should be the ultimate object of all Christian service.

4. Though the practice of Christianity may involve the most menial of tasks, all such practice is placed by the Bible on a very high plane. Observe how the practical section of Christian service begins at the peak of the Christian's consecration (12:1-2) and ends at the peak of God's glory (15:8-13). All the commands and exhortations are recorded in between. Read these two passages at this time.

5. Study the threefold outline at the bottom of the chart, beginning with Deadliness of Sin. Another way to word this outline is: Need of Salvation; Way of Salvation; Results of Salvation.

6. Some look on chapters 9-11 as parenthetical, because in these chapters Paul's subject is a special people—Israel —whereas in the sections preceding and following these chapters he speaks about *all* people and *all* Christians. But the Jews are brought into the discussion of the epistle in other parts of Romans, such as the first chapters, and Gentiles are very prominent in chapters 9-11. Therefore the outlines of survey Chart D consider these chapters to be an integral part of Paul's theme, not parenthetical. Your analysis of these chapters in later lessons will concern this point.

7. Study the other outlines shown on Chart D to help you get a mental image of the full scope of Paul's epistle.

Throughout this study guide the following terms will be used to represent individual units in the epistle:

    a. Division: These are the largest units. For Romans, there are four divisions: prologue; doctrinal; practical; epilogue. (See survey Chart D.)

    b. Section: These are the parts within a division, such as 1:18—3:20.

    c. Segment: A segment is a unit of study within a section, approximately the length of one chapter (e.g., 2:17—3:8).

    d. Paragraph: Parts of a segment.

    e. Verse: Parts of a paragraph.

B. Theme.

The central theme of Romans is the imparting of God's righteousness to the sinner who believes on the Lord Jesus Christ. Woven into this theme are such truths as: all are sinners; sin brings eternal death; there is only one way of salvation; God is no respecter of persons; salvation is a gift of God; and the power of God is the source of all Christian living.

C. Key Verses.

Because of the key words contained in 1:16-17, these verses may be considered key verses for Romans:

> For I am not ashamed of the gospel of Christ: for it is the power of God unto salvation to every one that believeth: to the Jew first, and also to the Greek. For therein is the righteousness of God revealed from faith to faith: as it is written, The just shall live by faith.

D. A Title for Romans.

During the course of your study various titles for Romans will suggest themselves. Use one of your own, preferably. The one given on survey Chart D is "God's Salvation for Sinners."

E. Key Words.

There are many important words in Romans. The following are definitely key words, used by Paul over and over again in his writing: law, righteousness, faith, believe, sin, death, flesh, all, impute, in Christ, Spirit. You may want to glance at an exhaustive concordance (e.g., Strong's) to see how often Paul uses these words in this one epistle.

F. The Place of Romans in Scripture.

In order to appreciate the important place which Romans occupies in Scripture, it is necessary to understand something of fallen man's utter lack of righteousness as revealed throughout human history.

A review of the moral history of the race as set forth in the books of the Bible up to the book of Romans shows that man is, and always has been, an utter failure as regards righteousness. When Adam was tempted in the Garden of Eden he proved himself a failure, and all of Adam's descendants have proved themselves failures under temptation. "All have sinned" (Rom. 3:23). "There is none righteous, no, not one" (Rom. 3:10).

From Adam to Abraham God patiently dealt with the sons of man, wooing them to His compassionate heart, giving them opportunity after opportunity to choose Him and His way, and so to find His favor. But the human race as a whole rejected Him, and the result was utter failure— failure so great that God "gave them up" and allowed them to go on in their own wicked ways (Rom. 1:24, 26, 28).

Then God tested the nation of Israel—the Jews. Everything was given them to afford a perfect opportunity to choose the righteous ways of God: special privileges, perfect instruction, marvelous revelations, miraculous protection and matchless covenants and promises. But here again we see utter and complete failure—failure so great that when they had crucified the Lord Jesus and refused to listen to the voice of the Holy Spirit through the apostles, God rejected them and scattered them throughout the earth, allowing them to go on in their own blindness and darkness.

In the book of Romans God is saying to the whole world—Jew and Gentile—that though they have failed to attain a righteousness acceptable to a holy God, this righteousness may be received from Him, through faith, in the person of His righteous Son.

G. Romans for Today.

The message of Romans is as applicable today as it was

19

when Paul wrote the letter. This is because the human heart has not changed; its needs are the same. And God has not changed; His gospel is the same.

> The divinely revealed gospel of God in Romans is the antidote for the babel of false gospels of our day or any day. Called the profoundest and yet the simplest document, the epistle is for sinful mankind **as it is**. It points out how lost, helpless humanity can find deliverance in Christ and what this deliverance includes. All focuses in Christ's cross. Christ's redemption is shown to be humanity's **only** hope. But what a glorious, exhilarating hope!*

As you study this very enlightening book of God, keep your spiritual eyes wide open to see what God has written. Don't evade the divine finger that points to sin. Don't turn away from words about the cross, blood, sacrifice and death, as ignoble and offensive as these are. If you are a Christian, be grateful that Christ died in your place, that the wrath of God was spent on Him. And in this wonderful book of doctrines don't overlook all it has to say about how God helps His children to live pleasing to Him. Believe it—really believe it—that God will never expect more of you in your daily living than what is possible with His help.

Review questions:

1. Each book of the Bible serves a particular function as part of the whole. What is Romans' main contribution?

_____

2. To whom was Romans written? _____

What was the occasion and purpose of its writing? _____

_____

3. What chapters are distinctly doctrinal? _____

4. What chapters are distinctly practical? _____

5. Complete the outline that begins: God's Holiness in Condemning Sin. Try to recall the chapter and verse

divisions for each section in the outline. _____

_____

6. See how much of survey Chart D you remember. Draw it out on a piece of paper.

*Merrill F. Unger, *Unger's Bible Handbook,* p. 607.

20

7. What are some of the key words of Romans? _____

_____

_____

8. Quote the key verses of Romans.

9. In your own words write out the theme of Romans. _____

_____

_____

Paul's Burden

PAUL'S EPISTLE TO THE ROMANS WAS
NOT A HASTILY WRITTEN NOTE, WHICH
IS APPARENT FROM THE INTRODUCTION.

There Paul carefully interweaves 273 Greek words into a beautiful pattern that includes greeting, testimony, doctrine and encouragement. This salutation is longer than that of any of the Pauline epistles. Compare it with a typical contemporary greeting: "Dear John: How are you doing? Fine I trust."

In the opening seventeen verses of Romans Paul shares with his readers the burden and conviction of his heart. The verses set the tone and introduce the theme of the entire epistle. The theme is that God offers salvation to everyone that believeth (1:16). The tone is a mixture of *awe* (e.g., "power of God," "Spirit of holiness" and "resurrection from the dead"); *urgency* to declare the gospel which lost souls need desperately to hear; *humility* of one who cherished the title "servant of Jesus Christ"; and *gratitude* to God for salvation and for the fellowship of saints.

Your study of these opening verses of Romans is a key to the study of all the segments that follow. Catch something of the fire, conviction and tenderness in Paul's heart at this point, and this mighty epistle will become more than just a book of doctrine.

I. PARAGRAPH DIVISIONS.

Each book of the Bible may be divided into segments, which are units of study as long as one chapter, or shorter or longer. Each segment in turn is divided into paragraphs. For each lesson of this manual the opening verse of each new paragraph will be given as a basis for study partitions.

Mark these in your Bible so that as you read the text you are always "paragraph conscious." This serves as a reminder and a help in seeing the "forest" as you look at the many "trees" in any one passage.

The paragraphs of the segment 1:1-17 begin at verses 1, 8, 16.

II. ANALYSIS.

1. The starting point in analysis is always that of reading through the entire passage without pausing. The purpose of this is to get an overview and major impressions, observe repeated words and phrases, and catch the tone or atmosphere of the passage. Browning's rule is "Image the whole, then execute the parts."

2. Throughout your study, keep pencil and paper handy to record observations along the way. One way to record the findings of your study is by the analytical chart. Simply draw a vertical rectangle on a piece of paper (8½x 11 inches), similar to that of Chart E. Mark off the paragraph divisions, recording the verse references. Use the space inside the rectangle to record words and phrases of the biblical text, and use the margins to write your own notes, outlines and comments. It will surprise you how much you will see in the Bible when you begin to record your observations. So, concerning any observation, jot it down!

The brief observations already recorded on Chart E suggest the kinds of notations you want to make on your own analytical chart. Follow the suggestions and questions given below to amplify the above mentioned observations, and to initiate new lines of study.

1. Analyze carefully the first paragraph. (In the AV it is all one sentence!) Underline in your Bible the strong words and phrases. Record on the analytical chart the things that are written about these: Paul, gospel of God, His Son.

What is written here about the humanity of Christ? _____

_____

About the deity of Christ? _____

_____

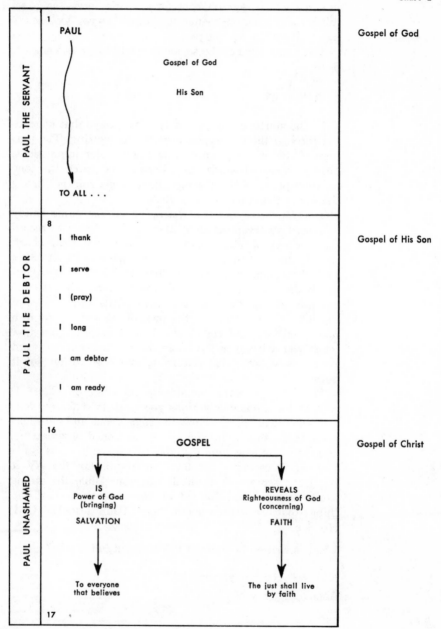

PAUL THE SERVANT

1
PAUL

Gospel of God

His Son

TO ALL . . .

Gospel of God

PAUL THE DEBTOR

8
I   thank

I   serve

I   (pray)

I   long

I   am debtor

I   am ready

Gospel of His Son

PAUL UNASHAMED

16
GOSPEL

IS
Power of God
(bringing)

SALVATION

To everyone
that believes

REVEALS
Righteousness of God
(concerning)

FAITH

The just shall live
by faith

17

Gospel of Christ

How important are such doctrines with reference to the gospel? _____

What is the full meaning of each of the following designations:

servant (1:1) _____

apostle (1:1) _____

prophets (1:2) _____

the called (1:6) _____

beloved (1:7) _____

saints (1:7) _____

2. Read the second paragraph (vv. 8-15) again, noting the many occurrences of the personal pronoun I. Develop the study recorded on Chart E. What would be known of Paul's character if these verses were all that was written of him?

List the qualities. _____

_____

3. The last paragraph, which contains the key verses for Romans, is a transition paragraph. How does it relate to

what goes before and to what follows? _____

_____

What are the strong words of this paragraph? _____

_____

Study the word diagram centering in GOSPEL, shown in the paragraph box 1:16-17 of analytical Chart E. What is

meant by verse 17? _____

_____

How is righteousness related to faith? (Note: The word "just" may be read "righteous"; read Hab. 2:4 for the source of the quote; cf. Gal. 3:11.) _____

What do you think is meant by the phrase "righteousness of God revealed from faith to faith" (1:17)? _____

4. Note the reference "to the Jew first, and also to the Greek (1:16). By "Greek" is meant all non-Jews. Paul here is not prescribing the order in which the gospel should be presented to the world. What he is saying is that Christ's gospel is God's power both to the Jews who by their heritage of law, temple, prophets and other ministers of the old covenant had first claim to the message of the new covenant; and to non-Jews as well.

5. List some important spiritual truths taught by this passage concerning such things as the way of salvation, Christian service, love, faith, prayer. _____

_____

_____

_____

6. What is taught about God in these verses? _____

_____

_____

About Jesus Christ? _____

_____

III. COMMENTS.

The heart of Paul's message concerned (1) God's righteousness, and (2) man's faith. Verse 17 of chapter 1, containing the unclear phrase "from faith to faith," reads thus in F. F. Bruce's expanded paraphrase:

> Because in this good news there is a revelation of God's righteousness—a way of righteousness based on the principle of faith, and offered to all men for acceptance by faith, in accordance

with the words of the prophet: "It is he who is righteous by faith that will live."*

A clue to the success of Paul as a witness for Christ wherever he went is to be found in his motivation. One aspect of that motivation is seen in the words "I am debtor" (1:14). "His desire to come to Rome is not merely to impart a gift; it is actually to pay a debt . . . . Paul meant to affirm that he felt under a solemn obligation to give to men of all races and classes and degrees of culture the gospel which had been committed to him as a sacred trust."†

Three times in this passage Paul makes use of the expression "I am":

a. "I am debtor" (1:14).

b. "I am ready" (1:15).

c. "I am not ashamed" (1:16).

Can each one of us say the same of ourselves? Do we really feel our indebtedness to the lost? Do we realize that we actually *owe* to souls numbered among the millions of those we call "heathen" the knowledge of the gospel of salvation, which has been entrusted to us to proclaim? Then are we ready (willing) to proclaim it to the full extent of our ability, as was Paul? And can we truly say "I am not ashamed of the gospel of God"? In any society, under any circumstances, are we ever ashamed to speak out and tell the good news to those we know are in need of salvation?

IV. SUMMARY.

Paul opened his letter on a bright positive note, emphasizing the good news or gospel. The three paragraphs may be outlined as shown below, based on what is said in each paragraph following the appearance of the word "gospel":

The message of the gospel (vv. 1-7)

The hearers of the gospel (vv. 8-15)

The power of the gospel (vv. 16-17)

*F. F. Bruce, *The Letters of Paul*, p. 183.

†Charles R. Erdman, *The Epistle of Paul to the Romans*, pp. 24-25.

The Pagan World and the Self-righteous Condemned

A FULL DISCOURSE ON SALVATION MUST

BEGIN WITH AN IDENTIFICATION OF THE

NEED OF SINFUL MAN FOR SALVATION.

For salvation means deliverance, which suggests both deliverance *from* and deliverance *unto*. Salvation is from darkness to light (I Peter 2:9); from guilt to pardon (Eph. 1:7); from slavery to freedom (Gal. 5:1); from death to life (Rom. 5:21). Thus Paul devotes much space at the beginning of his letter to write about sin—the deadliness of sin—the wrath of God revealed against sin. This, says Paul, is what all people need to be saved from.

Look at the survey Chart D and observe that the two parts of this lesson (1:18-32 and 2:1-16) are the first two of the four segments in the section called God's Holiness in Condemning Sin. This is an excerpt from Chart D:

FIRST EXCERPT FROM CHART D   **Chart F**

1:18	3:21	6:1	9:1	12:1 15:13
God's Holiness in Condemning Sin	God's Grace in Justifying Sinners	God's Power in Sanctifying Believers	God's Sovereignty in Saving Jew and Gentile	God's Glory the Object of Service

The first section (1:18—3:20) may be divided into four parts, studied in the lessons shown below:

The Pagan World Condemned   (1:18-32)   } Lesson 4
The Self-righteous Condemned   (2:1-16)
The Jew Condemned   (2:17—3:8) } Lesson 5
The Whole World Condemned   (3:9-20)

PART ONE: THE PAGAN WORLD CONDEMNED
(1:18-32).

I. PARAGRAPH DIVISIONS.

At verses 18, 24, 28.

II. ANALYSIS.

These verses represent the classic Bible passage referred to for answers to such questions as Are the heathen lost? and Is it fair that those who never in their lifetime hear the gospel message should be eternally condemned? Look for answers to these questions as you study this passage.
1. Read 1:18-23 very carefully. Compare the phrases "righteousness of God revealed" (1:17) and "wrath of God is revealed" (1:18). What is His righteousness a response to, and what is His wrath a response to? (Cf. Num. 32:14; Deut. 29:20; Zeph. 1:18.) _____

_____

Read the word "hold" (v. 18) as "hold down" or "suppress." Compare the beginning of the passage ("wrath," v. 18) with the end of the passage ("worthy of death," v. 32).
2. Sinners are without excuse for their sin if they refuse to respond to the light and revelation which God has given them, and if they make their own gods. The pagan world surely comes under this category. How much light is given such people, according to 1:19-20? _____
Read "manifest in them" as "visible to them." The question may be asked, Do any heathen people ever respond adequately to such light of nature and conscience? The answer is Yes, some do. It is these to whom God gives further light, such as the preached word by a missionary. The sovereign guidance of God, in decisions such as are made by mission boards as to where to send a missionary, is fully recognized by such a view of what happens to heathen who do respond favorably to first light.
3. List the various reactions of pagan sinners to God's revelation as given in verses 21-23. _____

_____

_____

4. God's response to the pagan reaction is described as "God gave them up unto" (1:24, 26, 28; cf. Gen. 6:3). "The Lord hands men over to the consequences of that which they have chosen for themselves."* Note that Paul cites again the basic sin in verses 25 and 28a. What is that sin? _____

_____

What kinds of sin does this sin generate? _____

_____

Account for such a variety of "degrees" of sin (e.g., murder as compared with pride). Do such sinners have any idea that severe judgment will come for their sin? _____

In other words, are they forewarned? See 1:32. _____

_____

5. Are the heathen (i.e., the unevangelized people) lost?

_____

Is God fair in His judgments against anyone who rejects whatever light God gives him? Justify your answer. _____

_____

III. COMMENTS.

Paul firmly declares that God's wrath is justly revealed against pagan sinners because God gives them sufficient knowledge of Himself to induce reverent worship and obedience, making this revelation of Himself both in their conscience (1:19) and through nature (1:20). But when men thus introduced to God refuse to worship and serve Him (1:21-23), God gives them up to their own ways (vv. 24-26), and those ways lead them into the fearful depths of iniquity pictured in verses 26-32.

Verses 21-23 describe various stages of Gentile (non-Jew) world apostasy. Look at Chart G and trace the seven steps by which the heathen world descended from the knowledge of the true God to the most degraded idolatry.

*Charles F. Pfeiffer and Everett F. Harrison (eds.), *The Wycliffe Bible Commentary*, p. 1187.

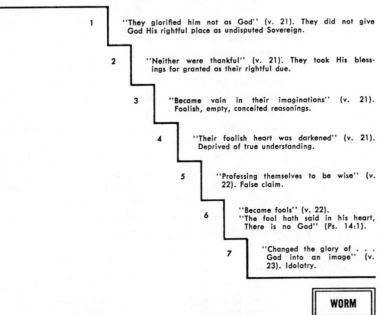

GOD

THE WORLD HAD RECEIVED THE KNOWLEDGE OF GOD (v. 21), AND YET—

1   "They glorified him not as God" (v. 21). They did not give God His rightful place as undisputed Sovereign.

2   "Neither were thankful" (v. 21). They took His blessings for granted as their rightful due.

3   "Became vain in their imaginations" (v. 21). Foolish, empty, conceited reasonings.

4   "Their foolish heart was darkened" (v. 21). Deprived of true understanding.

5   "Professing themselves to be wise" (v. 22). False claim.

6   "Became fools" (v. 22). "The fool hath said in his heart, There is no God" (Ps. 14:1).

7   "Changed the glory of . . . God into an image" (v. 23). Idolatry.

WORM

At the top of Chart G is the word GOD to indicate that mankind started with the knowledge and worship of the true and living God. At the bottom of the diagram is the word WORM to indicate that mankind, in their departure from God, descended so low that they actually came to worship the image of a worm—"creeping things" (v. 23). What a tragic fall! From the living God, Maker of heaven and earth, to the image of a worm. This is the religious history of the race. The development has not been upward, as ethical evolutionists declare, but downward.

Notice also that the first steps away from God were negative. "They glorified him *not*" (v. 21). They were *not* thankful (v. 21). It is a dangerous thing to neglect God and His claims. Sins of omission are as great as sins of commission.

Notice in verse 23 that when men had at last descended to idolatry there was still a downward trend. They first changed the glory of the uncorruptible God into an image made like to corruptible man. That would seem to be low enough, but they went on to make images of birds (creatures of the air), then to four-footed beasts (creatures of the earth), and then to creeping things.

The "wrath of God" must be understood as His hatred of sin, not of the sinner. He loves the sinner. He loves sinners so much that He gave His only begotten Son to die for them, but His holiness and justice demand that He hate and deal with sin. And so He beseeches sinners, whom He loves, to turn to Him and be separated from sin, which He hates. As a mother hates and fights the disease which would destroy her child, so is God's attitude toward sin which would destroy the soul.

Verses 28-32 present the revolting picture of man after this threefold "giving up" of God, the climax being seen in the statement of verse 32, that those guilty of these crimes commit them with the full knowledge of the penalty of death which they deserve and, worst of all, they rejoice in others, and encourage others, who practice the same sins.

> This dark and painful picture of the pagan world . . . is a picture of the degradation into which mankind ever sinks when turning from the truth of God and no longer restrained by his grace. It was given as the reason why Paul gloried in the gospel and desired to have it proclaimed in Rome. It should arouse all Christian readers to-day to hasten the preaching of this gospel as the only hope of the human race.†

PART TWO: THE SELF-RIGHTEOUS CONDEMNED (2:1-16).

I. PARAGRAPH DIVISIONS.

At verses 1, 5, 12.

II. ANALYSIS.

The Jew is not specifically addressed in this chapter until verse 17. The address "thou . . . O man" of verse 1 is general and may be intended to include all self-righteous moralists. By definition in this context, a self-righteous moralist is a legalist who believes that the life acceptable to God is the zealous performance of that which man con-

†Charles R. Erdman, *The Epistle of Paul to the Romans*, p. 31.

siders to be morally right. Paul before his conversion was such a man.

It appears that Paul had Jews particularly in mind when he wrote about self-righteous moralists in verses 1-16. Such Jews are those who base their salvation on the fact that the law which they observe must save them because it is God's special gift to them. In order to derive a larger application from this passage, the following questions use the terms self-righteous and moralist, rather than Jew. As you analyze this passage keep in mind the title "The Self-righteous Condemned."

1. By whom is the self-righteous moralist condemned in the first paragraph (2:1-4)? _____

How does man fall short as a judge of human conduct?

_____

Why does Paul mention the goodness of God in this context of judgment (v. 4)? _____

_____

2. Read 2:5-11. By what is the moralist judged, according to verse 6? _____

What is the sin of the moralist? (Note the "thy" of v. 5.)

_____

What are the two judgments? _____

What kind of life brings on each judgment? _____

_____

Why the emphasis of no distinction in judgment in verses 9-11? _____

_____

3. Read 2:12-16. Look for the third reference to judgment "according to." On the basis of this, complete an outline for this segment with the title "The Self-righteous Condemned." _____

_____

Treat verses 14-15 as parenthetical. Interpret the entire paragraph in the light of this main core:

> The doers of the law shall be justified . . . in the day when God shall judge the secrets of men by Jesus Christ according to my gospel (vv. 13-16).

This tremendous truth is merely introduced at this point. Paul has much more to say about it in the chapters to follow. What brings death and judgment (v. 12)? _____

_____

What brings justification (v. 13)? _____

_____

(Definition: Justification is the judicial act of God in declaring a sinner righteous. This subject will be expanded later.)

III. COMMENTS.

In chapter 1 Paul speaks principally of the guilt of the Gentiles, the pagan nations living in unrestrained sin. He proves that they are in desperate need of the righteousness of God because they are sinners without excuse. Their sin is that, although God makes Himself known to them through their conscience and through nature, they refuse to worship and serve Him.

In chapter 2 Paul shows how these same things are true of any self-righteous people, particularly the Jews. The Jews knew God not only by the revelation He had given of Himself to all men in their conscience and through nature, but they had been made intimately acquainted with His character and will through the written law given through Moses. But this superior knowledge, and the favor which God had shown to the Jews in making them a select nation to be His representative people, had not led them to worship and serve Him. Though they observed the outward ceremonies which God had appointed, their hearts were far from Him. God's favor had filled them with pride and caused them to set themselves up as judges of other people, to whom they were in the habit of referring as "the dogs of the Gentiles."

As though speaking to some individual Jew who had been listening with relish to his arraignment of the Gentile sinners in the last part of chapter 1, Paul begins, in verse 1 of chapter 2, to show such a self-righteous man how inexcusable is his attitude of judging other sinners, because he too is a sinner—in the same way as they.

Men's judgment of one another is unbecoming and inaccurate, but we are sure, Paul says, that the judgment of God is according to truth, and in accordance with guilt, based on facts and according to our just deserts (v. 2). Because the judgment of God is according to truth and justice, the sinning Jew must not think that he, any more than the sinning Gentile, shall escape this judgment (v. 3).

The Jews had misinterpreted the goodness, forbearance and long-suffering which God had shown toward them as a nation. God had been trying by His goodness to induce them to turn from sin (v. 4).

The Jews, however, had come to think that because they were the chosen representatives of God they occupied such a place of privilege that they could do as they pleased and be immune from the consequences of sin. Really, Paul told them, the hard impenitent attitude of their heart was just treasuring up for themselves wrath in that day when God's real attitude against sin is to be revealed (v. 5).

In the next eleven verses, 6-16, Paul sets forth these two great principles of God's judgment:

1. Each man will be judged according to his deeds (vv. 6-11).
2. Each man will be judged according to his light (vv. 12-16).

Some erroneously interpret verses 6-11 to teach salvation by works instead of by faith. But Paul is not speaking here of salvation but of judgment. He says in verses 6-7 that God will render eternal life to them who by patient continuance in well-doing seek for glory, honor and immortality. But he does not say God will render them eternal life *because* of their well-doing. Later in the book he shows that God gives eternal life to men because of their *faith* in Christ. Here he is saying that the deeds mentioned in verse 7 indicate the attitude of heart which will eventually receive eternal life, while the deeds mentioned in verse 8 express the attitude of heart which will eventually receive indignation and wrath, tribulation and anguish. Griffith Thomas says, "He is dealing with the *result,* not the *process;* the *goal,* not the *way.* What he says is that no one can be saved eventually apart from doing good, the power to do which comes, as will be shown in its proper place, through the gospel."

As the *ground* of God's judgment is to be works, so the *rule* of God's judgment is to be light—the light which each one severally has enjoyed (v. 12-16).

Those who have never known the written law, such as was given to the Jews, will be judged, but not by that law. They will be judged as to whether they have been faithful to the light given to *them*, through nature and their own conscience (vv. 14-15). But the Jews, who have the law, will be judged by the law. They will be judged as to whether they have been faithful to the light given them through the law (vv. 12-13).

To the very pertinent question Why should we take the gospel to those who have never heard it? A. Berkeley Mickelsen gives the following answer:

> First of all, because God has commanded us to do so (Mt 28:19, 20; Acts 1:8). Secondly, it is essential because of who God is that every individual be confronted with the knowledge of God (Isa 11:9; Hab 2:14; Isa 45:5, 6; 52:10; 66:18, 19; II Thess 1:8) and have opportunity to commit himself to Him, and to increase in knowledge of Him (Jn 14:7; 17:3; II Cor 2:14; Tit 1:16; I Jn 2:3-6; 5:19, 20; Phil 3:8-10; II Pet 3:18). Finally, it is essential because of who Christ is—the climax of God's revelation (Heb. 1:1, 2).‡

IV. SUMMARY OF 1:18—2:16.

The pagan world is condemned in the sight of God not because of ignorance of God but because their reaction to the light given them concerning God is one of rejection, unthankfulness, vanity, presumption and evil deeds. They are all without excuse.

Self-righteous moralists are condemned by God, even though they absolve themselves. Moralists presume to be judges, but sinners cannot truly judge. The only source of infallible judgment is God Himself, who is righteous, fair and also good. All divine recompense is based on man's works, according to the light given him. The self-righteous man will be judged for his own sins. The fact that he keeps laws which the heathen know nothing about, will not save him in the last day. Divine judgment of men is individual, absolute, just. No other relationship can exist between Creator and creature, or utter chaos would be the result.

‡A. Berkeley Mickelsen in *Wycliffe Bible Commentary*, p. 1189.

The Jew Condemned;
The Whole World Condemned

EVERYONE STANDS GUILTY BEFORE GOD,

THE HOLY ONE, BECAUSE EACH ONE HAS

TRANSGRESSED THE HOLY LAW OF GOD.

People react differently to the sense of guilt within them which urges them to find hope. Some resort to idolatry and corruption (1:18-32). Others seek to justify themselves by a self-righteous morality—the "I'm a good citizen" type (2:1-16). A third group finds its haven in formal religion, willing to pay any price of outward worship. We have already studied the first two groups; in Part One of this lesson we will see why religionists are condemned. Part Two is devoted to Paul's concluding words of this larger section, wherein he shows that the whole world is condemned—"There is none righteous, no, not one" (3:10).

This lesson may be studied as two separate units, Part One and Part Two. Other lessons in the manual may likewise be divided into smaller study units.

PART ONE: THE JEW CONDEMNED (2:17—3:8).

I. PARAGRAPH DIVISIONS.

At verses 2:17, 25; 3:1.

II. ANALYSIS.

One important thing to remember as you study this passage is that it may be given a wider application than what the word Jew suggests. Paul at this point particularly singles out the Jew because he has already written about the guilt of the non-Jew or Gentile. The sin of the Jew here is that of outward religion devoid of inner spirit. Because such a sin is found universally, it may be said that in these twenty-one verses is recorded God's indictment against all sinners who count on their religion to save them.

First read the passage in a paraphrase version (e.g., William's *New Testament in the Language of the People*°).

Then return to your study text and determine what each paragraph is saying. Record this below, in a few words:

2:17-24 _____

_____

2:25-29 _____

_____

3:1-8 _____

_____

The third paragraph may be a little more difficult to understand because of the way it is worded. Refer back to the paraphrase for help. The word "commend" (3:5) should be translated "brings out" (meaning, "brings out by way of contrast").

1. The title of this segment is "The Jew Condemned." Keep this in mind in all of your study, noting what each paragraph says about this condemnation.

2. See 2:17-24. Note how the paragraph opens with reference to the name of Jew ("called a Jew") and closes with reference to "name of God." According to the verses in between, how is such a religion guilty of blasphemy? ____

_____

List the boasts and privileges of the Jews (2:17-20). ____

_____

In light of these, what basic sin are such Jews guilty of, referred to in verses 21-23? _____

_____

3. Note how non-Jews enter into Paul's discussion of this section on Jews: "Gentiles" (2:24), "the uncircumcision"

°This modern version of the New Testament is published by Moody Press in an individual edition and also in the parallel edition The Four Translation New Testament.

(3:26), "the world" (3:6). What is the point made in each case? _____

_____

4. See 2:25-29. What is the Jews' sin in verses 28-29? ___

_____

How is this different from the basic sin of the first paragraph? _____

_____

Is Paul tearing down Judaism itself? See 2:25. _____

_____

How does Paul identify a true Jew (2:29)? _____

_____

5. See 3:1-8. Note three different references to Jews in this paragraph: individuals ("the Jews," 3:1), the Old Testament Israel as a whole ("them," 3:2), and unbelieving Jews ("some did not believe," 3:3).

In this paragraph Paul concludes his point that the Jew is condemned by stating that the Jew is condemned *absolutely*. That is,

    a. God's judgment of individual Jews does not detract from the privileges and preeminence He gave Israel as a nation (3:1-4).

    b. God's judgment of individual Jews is not lessened because Israel is His chosen people (3:5-8).

    c. God's judgment of individual Jews is never relative —it is always absolutely just and true (e.g., 3:5-6).

After you have read the above statements, go back to the biblical text and note the way Paul brings out the above points. In what way is this paragraph a conclusion

to the theme of the segment 2:17—3:8? _____

_____

6. Chart H shows some outlines of this segment. After you have read each outline, refer back to the text to see where and how it is developed. (This method of study is called *deductive*, that is, starting with an outline or conclusion, and observing how it is supported by the text.)

THE JEW CONDEMNED

2:17	2:25	3:1 3:8
FOR DISOBEDIENCE —not applying the truth	**FOR HYPOCRISY** —outward show —praise of men	**ABSOLUTELY** —changeless, just, true
"Thou art called a Jew" (2:17).	"He is a Jew, which is one inwardly" (2:29).	"What advantage then hath the Jew?" (3:1).
Privileges — Works Are Are Bright Evil	Heart — Works Is Appear Sinful Righteous	
Boast of the Jew → SIN:	Identification of a True Jew → SIN:	Chief Privilege of the Jew → SIN:

7. From your study of 2:17—3:8, write a list of symptoms of the evil of "religiosity." _____

_____

How should a Christian witness to someone who is counting on his religion for salvation? _____

_____

III. COMMENTS.

Beginning at 2:17 Paul shows that the great opportunities which had been given to the Jews had placed upon them great obligations. They were indeed the chosen people of God—chosen to represent Him and acquaint other peoples with His character and will. They were indeed familiar with His will and, so far as knowledge went, they were in a position to be "a guide of the blind, a light of them which are in darkness, an instructor of the foolish, a teacher of babes" (2:19-20). But Paul charges that the Jews had sinned in that they had not practiced what they preached (2:21-24). They had sinned not through ignorance but through willfulness. Their *knowledge* was correct but their *deeds* were evil. It is not simply *knowing* God's will which is required, but it is *doing* God's will which is pleasing in His sight (read in this connection Deut. 4:1; 5:1; 6:1, 3, emphasizing the words "do" and "keep").

The sin of the Jews had not only brought the condemnation of God upon themselves but it had brought reproach upon the name of God (2:23-24). Of this Charles Erdman writes:

> In ancient days the Gentiles beheld the misery of Israel and blasphemed God as one who was not able to protect his own people and worshipers; in the time of Paul, the Gentiles were blaspheming the name of God as One who could not keep from sin his chosen people, the custodians of his law and the special objects of his grace. So to-day reproach is often brought upon the name of Christ by the inconsistencies of Christians.†

The rite of circumcision in the Jewish religion originated to symbolize Israel's covenant relation to Jehovah. Read Genesis 17:7-14 and Romans 4:11, which record the initiation and interpretation of this rite, respectively. Circumcision of the flesh was merely an outward sign to express an inward reality. Those who are truly circumcised are God's children—whether Jew or Gentile—who trust in Him and obey His will.

In answering the question "What advantage then hath the Jew?" (3:1), Paul recognizes the fact known by all that God sovereignly gave to the Jews the honor and favor of being the depository of God's Scriptures, most of which were also written by Jews. But Paul has in mind an advantage more efficacious and fruitful than that. In answering the question he anticipates a theme which he later on develops in the epistle (chap. 11). His answer applies to the Jews as a nation. In the oracles or prophetic disclosures of the Scriptures which God committed to the Jews, He made many great promises to them, many of them unconditional promises. And the unbelief and unfaithfulness of *some* Jews could not make God unfaithful concerning His promises to Israel as a nation. He would keep such unconditional promises (3:3-4). Ever since the time of Abraham, Israel has been God's chosen people. God has not cast away His people (11:2). True Israel has a glorious future (11:26), "for this is my covenant unto them" (11:27). Advantage? Yes, much, says Paul. But

†Charles R. Erdman, *The Epistle of Paul to the Romans*, p. 44.

each Jew is guilty who does not personally render proportionate faithfulness and service to God as Lord.

PART TWO: THE WHOLE WORLD CONDEMNED
(3:9-20).

I. PARAGRAPH DIVISIONS.

At verses 9, 13, 19.

II. ANALYSIS.

Everyone is guilty! This is the final verdict rendered in God's court of justice where man is tried and found wanting. Romans 3:9-20 records this verdict which can be contested only by those who defy God.

This segment is the summation of the case which Paul began describing at 1:18. He showed the pagan world condemned (1:18-32), the self-righteous condemned (2:1-16), and the Jew, representing formal religionists, condemned (2:17—3:8). Each sinner fits into one of these categories, so Paul is now ready to conclude his theme on the note of universal condemnation.

1. After you have marked the paragraph divisions in your Bible, read the segment at least twice, noting especially the atmosphere of *finality* about the passage.

2. Observe that the word "sin" appears in the opening and closing verses of the segment. Write out a definition of sin in your own words. _____

_____

This entire segment is about sin—it is for sin that the whole world is condemned.

3. Read 3:9-12 again. One possible free rendering of verse 9*a* is: "What then are we to conclude? Do we (i.e., all of us) have anything in ourselves to shield us from God's wrath?"‡ This concords with the phrase "under sin" of 9*b*, which means under the power and control of sin.

Note that Paul quotes Old Testament Scripture to support his statement of 9*b* that *all* are under sin. All of 3:10-18 is comprised of Old Testament quotes. How is Paul's exposition strengthened by his quoting Scripture? _____

_____

‡For a discussion of the original text here, see Charles F. Pfeiffer and Everett F. Harrison (eds.), *The Wycliffe Bible Commentary*, p. 1191.

Read Psalm 14:1-3. Note the universal phrase "children of men" in Psalm 14:2. ·

Observe that the underlying spiritual disease of all mankind is this: "None . . . doeth good" (3:12). That is, there is no righteousness in the heart of man.

4. Read 3:13-18. In verses 9-12 Paul shows sin to be universal. Now he shows it to be thorough and total. What

parts of the body are mentioned in each line? _____

_____

Determine what the symbolical intent is in each case, and record an outline for this paragraph in the space provided in Chart I. Read the Old Testament passages which Paul quotes.

WORK CHART FOR ROMANS 3   Chart I

Old Testament passage	Romans 3	Symbol	Meaning	Outline
Psalm 5:9	13a			
Psalm 140:3	13b			
Psalm 10:7	14			
Isaiah 59:7	15			
59:7	16			
59:8	17			
Psalm 36:1	18			

5. Spend a little more time pondering the meaning of the phrase "fear of God" in verse 18. What kind of fear is

thus required of all men? _____

_____

_____

6. Read 3:19-20. Note the repeated word "law." The law of God—written or unwritten, understood or not understood—is the standard by which all lives are judged by God. This is why *all* the world is "guilty before God." Read Psalm 143:2 and Galatians 2:16 in connection with verse 20. A paraphrase of 20*b* is "The law brings men's sin to light and teaches them that they are sinners."

Think of "the law" here as referring to the Ten Commandments. Has anyone other than Jesus kept the whole

law? _____

Note by James 2:10 that to break one law is to be guilty

of breaking all. Why is this? _____

Is God's law good when it exposes our sin and condemns

us? _____

What is the main purpose of God's law? _____

_____

Read Romans 7:7; Galatians 3:24; I John 3:4 for help in answering these questions.

7. What is the strength of the phrase "in his sight" (3:20)?

_____

How does this substantiate the indictment Everyone is

guilty? _____

_____

8. Write a list of five vital truths taught by 3:9-20. _____

_____

_____

_____

_____

_____

III. COMMENTS.

After writing that *all* have sinned (3:9-12), and that such sin is totally cancerous and God-defying (3:13-18), Paul clearly records the verdict "Guilty before God" (3:19).

In these last verses he not only pronounces God's final verdict upon sinners, but declares man to be helpless and hopeless as well. The law cannot help him because the very purpose of the law is to reveal sin, not to relieve it. The law is God's measuring rod, His standard of righteousness. It shows what a man would have to be in order to be right with God. He would have to keep the law perfectly from the beginning to the end of life, in thought, word and deed, even as Jesus Christ kept it in every particular. But that is impossible for fallen man. By the deeds of the law man may be justified in his own sight and in the sight of his fellowmen, but not in God's sight.

It is clear at this point in Paul's epistle that God's law —whether it is the law written in the heart (Rom. 2:15), or the law written on tablets of stone—cannot save a man. If such a one is to be justified there must be some other way than through such law. What that other way is, Paul presents in the next two and a half chapters (3:21—5:21). The diagnosis of man's fatal disease has been described: the *heart cannot do good* (3:12). It is not righteous, nor does it have the power to attain righteousness. In the next chapters the prescription of cure is written, telling how sinful man can be given a heart of righteousness. No diagnosis without an offer of cure—such is the method of the holy *and* gracious God.

Justification Defined and Illustrated

ALL THE WORLD IS GUILTY BEFORE GOD,

BECAUSE ALL HAVE SINNED, AND ALL

HAVE FALLEN SHORT OF GOD'S GLORY.

"But now," writes Paul, "a way to get right with God has been revealed . . . provided by God, through faith in Jesus Christ, for all who believe in Him"° (3:21-22). This is the bright message of this second main section of Romans (3:21—5:21). Compare this section of the epistle with the first, as shown by Chart J, an excerpt from survey Chart D.

SECOND EXCERPT FROM CHART D   Chart J

1:18	3:21 5:21
God's Holiness in Condemning Sin	God's Grace in Justifying Sinners
S I N	SALVATION
God's Righteousness IN LAW	God's Righteousness IMPUTED
The Need of Salvation	The Way of Salvation

The tone of the first section was that of hopelessness. Any honest soul has to admit that there is not even a shimmer of light in the verdict "Guilty before God" (3:19). However that is not the last word from God. "But!" writes Paul (3:21a). Sometimes this small word "but" is a tragic word in Scripture. In this context it is a beacon of hope,

°F. F. Bruce, *The Letters of Paul*, p. 191.

pointing the eyes of the seeking soul to the way of salvation which the next chapters describe.

Two lessons in this study guide will be devoted to the section 3:21—5:21. Keep the outline in Chart K in mind as you study these chapters.

GOD'S GRACE IN JUSTIFYING SINNERS

Chart K

3:21 3:31	4:1 4:25	5:1 5:21
Justification Defined	Justification Illustrated	Justification's Fruits
Lesson 6		Lesson 7

PART ONE: JUSTIFICATION DEFINED (3:21-31).

I. PARAGRAPH DIVISIONS.

At verses 21, 27.

II. ANALYSIS.

Since definitions are in order at this time, it would be well to look into the meaning of the new theological words which Paul introduces in the section 3:21—5:21. Brief definitions are given below. As you study the text, you will find more truths suggested by the words in their context.

A. Justification (3:24, 26, 28).

In justification God *declares* a sinner righteous on the basis of his faith in Jesus Christ. Such a believer is legally declared to be in good standing with God. Whenever you read the word "justify" in the Bible, associate the word "righteous" with it, for the root of the Greek word translated "justify" is the very word translated "righteous." Read the following verses and note what each says about justification: Romans 5:1, 9; I Corinthians 6:11; I Timothy 3:16; Titus 3:7.

B. Redemption (3:24).

Christ's work of redemption for a soul is the offering of His life as a ransom, to give (1) deliverance from the penalty of the law, sin as a power, and the bondage of

47

Satan; and (2) release to a new relationship to God and a new life in Christ. Read the following verses and note what each verse teaches regarding these phases of redemption: ransom (I Cor. 6:20; Eph. 1:7; I Tim. 2:6; I Peter 1:18-19); deliverance (Gal. 3:13; Titus 2:14; Heb. 9:11-14); release (Rev. 5:9).

C. Propitiation (3:25).

Propitiation is not man's appeasement of God's wrath for sin, but God's merciful provision of forgiveness for that sin. (Cf. Heb. 2:17.) The shedding of Christ's blood effected this propitiation. Read Hebrews 9:5 and note the reference to the mercy seat, which in the Old Testament was the place where the high priest sprinkled blood to provide a sacrifice for the people's sins. The Greek word translated "mercyseat" is the same word translated "propitiation" in Romans 3:25.

D. Remission (3:25).

In the ten appearances of this word in the New Testament, the word "sins" is always included (e.g., "remission of sins"). Remission of sins is the canceling, pardoning, passing over of sins against the soul, made possible by the shedding of blood (cf. Heb. 9:22). Christ "appeared to put away sin by the sacrifice of himself" (Heb. 9:26b).

Now read 3:24-25 in the light of the above definitions, and observe the interrelations of these four works of Christ in behalf of the sinner.
1. Read 3:21-26 again. Note that in the King James Version this paragraph is all one sentence. What is the core

(main subject, main verb) of the sentence? _____

_____

Note how the sentence builds up, clause by clause.
2. Read 3:27-31. What point is established here about the

law? _____

_____

3. Two word studies are recommended for this segment. The words are:

righteousness (include also "justify," since the root of
this word is "righteous")

faith   (include also "believe")

Note how often these words are repeated in the segment.

Write a list of all the things taught about each. _____

_____

_____

_____

III. COMMENTS.

In the first section of the book of Romans God is seen as
the righteous Judge justly pronouncing sentence upon
guilty man. But in this second division of the book God
is seen as the merciful Saviour offering a pardon to guilty
helpless man. He offers it to all men because there is no
difference. All have sinned and come short of the glory
and approval of God (3:22-23), so all men need pardon.
When Paul says, "There is no difference" he does not
mean that all men have sinned equally. But all have sinned
and are therefore equally in need of the pardon which
God is offering.

In the six verses of 3:21-26 (which constitute the very
core of the epistle to the Romans, the very heart of the
gospel) is answered the most important question which
can be asked: How can a man be right with God? How
can one who is guilty of sin be forgiven, pardoned and
declared righteous?

Paul here answers that question by saying that through
the atoning work of Christ a righteousness has been provided for unrighteous man, and is offered as a free gift to
all who will believe.

Verse 25 says that the reason God set forth Christ to be
a propitiatory sacrifice was primarily to declare or demon-
strate His own righteousness in forgiving sins. What about
sins committed before the time of Christ? Of this, A.
Berkeley Mickelsen writes,

> But did God **let go unpunished the sins which happened** before
> Christ's death? The objective, public death of Christ at Calvary
> proves that the Lord did not let these sins go unpunished. We know
> that he was dealing with human sin there—with the past sins of
> mankind as well as with those presently being carried out, and

49

those yet to be committed—because he declared it through his apostles and prophets. These past sins were done **in the sphere of God's forbearance** (Rom 3:25). The Lord did not forget these sins, although he did not deal with them immediately.†

Justification by faith does not make God's law of none effect—it rather establishes the law (3:31). For the sinner who comes by faith to Jesus is confessing his guilt and acknowledging that he is justly condemned by the law.

PART TWO: JUSTIFICATION ILLUSTRATED
(4:1-25).

An effective way to teach Bible doctrines is by illustrations. Paul was aware of this when he wrote chapter 4. He had just defined and described justification (3:21-31). Now he would choose one man out of Israel's history—Abraham—and illustrate how and why he was justified.

The fact that Paul chose an Old Testament example of justification rather than a contemporary example, shows that this doctrine is universal and timeless. God has justified men who believed before Christ's time as well as after Christ's time.

I. PARAGRAPH DIVISIONS.

At verses 1, 9, 13, 16.

II. ANALYSIS.

1. Read the segment paragraph by paragraph, noting that the common theme illustrated in Abraham's life is that justification comes by faith. Then read the paragraphs separately to discover what different aspect of that theme is presented by each paragraph. Record your observations below (one example is given).

4:1-8: Justification is *not by works.*

9-12: _____

13-15: _____

16-25: _____

Concerning the second paragraph, keep in mind that circumcision was a sign (4:11) of Israel's covenant relationship to God.

†A. Berkeley Mickelsen in *The Wycliffe Bible Commentary,* p. 1193.

2. Note the similar phrases in verses 3 and 22. The word "imputed" of verse 22 translates the same Greek word as "counted" (v. 3). Thus imputation brings a *legal* standing of righteousness (cf. Philemon 18; I Cor. 1:30; II Cor. 5:21 for further light about this aspect of justification).

3. Note the suggestions of obstacles to faith in verses 18-21. Observe the contrast "weak in faith" (4:19) and "strong in faith" (4:20). What is the strength of "fully persuaded"

(4:21)? _____

_____

Note that Abraham and believers today are identified in the same group by verses 23-24. How is Christ's resurrection a basis for our justification (4:25)? _____

_____

III. COMMENTS.

Justification is apart from works (4:1-8); apart from religion (4:9-12); and apart from the law (4:13-15). And justification is not exclusive in its availability: it is *for all* who believe (4:16-25).

A. Apart from Works (4:1-8).

Paul turns to the Old Testament for confirmation that this gospel of justification by faith which he preaches is no new thing. On the contrary, it is God's established method of dealing with man from the first.

He first cites the case of Abraham, the founder of the Israelitish nation, who was known as "the friend of God." The question is How was he accepted or justified? Was it by works which he had done, or was it by believing God? The answer is stated clearly in verse 3: "Abraham believed God, and it was counted unto him for righteousness."

A laborer does not receive his wages or "reward" by grace ("grace" means unmerited favor). He merits it. He has earned it and can claim it as a debt owed him (4:4). But a sinner does not *merit* justification as payment of a debt. Therefore if he receives justification at all it must necessarily be "of grace," just a free gift from God. Abraham did not *earn* righteousness; he received it as a free gift.

Not only does Abraham's experience prove that justification is by faith and not by works, but Paul gives the testimony of David, Israel's greatest king, to this same blessed truth (4:6-8). David describes the blessed state of a man with no righteousness of his own, but to whom God "imputes" righteousness as a free gift, not because of any works which he has done (4:6). Such a man actually has iniquities and sins, but God has forgiven them, covered them. He does not impute these sins to him, but He imputes His own righteousness to him (4:7-8).

B. Apart from Religion (4:9-12).

Paul, having shown in the first eight verses of this chapter that justification is entirely apart from works, now proceeds to illustrate from Abraham's experience that justification is also entirely apart from ordinances of religion. He does this in order to show that justification by faith is for all, both Jew and Gentile; for those who had received the ordinance of circumcision and for those who had not (4:9).

At the time Abraham was justified he had not practiced any particular religious rites or ceremonies to commend him to God. Read Genesis 15:1-6 and observe that it was at this time that Abraham "believed in the LORD; and he counted it to him for righteousness" (Gen. 15:6). Circumcision came many years later, when it was prescribed as "a seal of the righteousness of the faith which he had yet being uncircumcised" (4:11). So Abraham was justified *before* he was circumcised, proving that justification is entirely independent of, and apart from, ordinances. Abraham was not justified because he was circumcised, but he was circumcised because he was justified and had been chosen of God to be His special representative. So now, a man is not justified because he joins the church or submits to the ordinance of baptism or any other ordinance. God justifies a sinner because he believes in Jesus Christ as the propitiatory sacrifice for sin. When he later joins the church and observes the ordinances it is *because* he has been justified and made God's child.

C. Apart from the Law (4:13-15).

As Abraham was not justified by works or by observing ordinances, neither was it through the law that he was accepted of God and given the promise that he should be the heir of the world (4:13). This is necessarily so because this promise was given to Abraham four hundred years before the Mosaic law was given (Gal. 3:17). Also the law was given to one nation, Israel, and if justification were by that law then only Israelites could be justified and God's promise of justification by faith, given long before the law, would be made of none effect (4:17).

> "Faith" and "promise" belong to a different domain from that of "law." The latter would exclude the former, and make them of no effect. The real effect of law is to bring condemnation . . . For this reason it was the plan of God to condition his great blessings not upon obedience to law but upon faith . . . and such a system made the fulfillment of the promise possible, not only to those who had the Mosaic law, but to all persons who, by their faith in God, are true children of Abraham.‡

Notice the character of Abraham's faith. Read verse 19 and consider how unlikely it would seem to human reason that Abraham and Sarah should have a son. But Abraham's eyes were upon "God, who quickeneth the dead, and calleth those things which be not as though they were" (4:17). He believed God's word regardless of all seeming impossibilities. Abraham did not require explanations or proofs before he would believe God's word. God had said it, and that was enough for him. That is the kind of faith which is imputed for righteousness (4:22).

IV. SUMMARY.

The good news for the people of the world, all of whom are guilty before God because of their sin, is that God in His grace offered His Son as a sacrifice to pay the penalty of sin. He who places his faith in Jesus Christ is counted as righteous, and thus receives the gift of eternal life. Abraham believed God, and his faith (not works, nor religion, nor law) was counted unto him for righteousness. "God will accept us in the same way He accepted Abraham —when we believe the promises of God Who brought back Jesus our Lord from the dead" (4:24, Living Letters).

‡ Charles R. Erdman, *The Epistle of Paul to the Romans*, p. 58.

Fruits of Justification

THE STUDY OF ROMANS 5 SHOULD BE A

HEARTENING EXPERIENCE BECAUSE THIS

CHAPTER DESCRIBES GOD'S BLESSINGS.

In this lesson we are calling these blessings *fruits* of justification, to suggest the Christian's *partaking* of such gifts of God.

I. PARAGRAPH DIVISIONS.

At verses 1, 6, 12. (The paragraph 5:12-21 may be divided into three smaller paragraphs, beginning at verses 12, 15, 18.)

II. ANALYSIS.

After reading the entire chapter at one time, aim your concentrated study at the smaller units of paragraphs. Suggestions for study are given below.
1. Read 5:1-5. Observe the frequency of the pronoun "we." Compare the next two paragraphs with this, concerning the person. Read the paragraph aloud using the singular I, and you will realize more pointedly how all these fruits are yours personally. Record a list of the fruits of justification. _____

_____

_____

What is meant by "we have peace with God" (5:1)? Observe the sequence beginning with tribulations. (The word "experience" of 5:4 may be read as "tested character.")

How does each discipline produce the next discipline?

_____

_____

2. Read 5:6-11. Notice references to death, particularly Christ's death, in each verse. What is the core (main subject, main verb) of verse 6? _____

_____

Compare this core with the core of the opening verses of the first paragraph (5:1-5). _____

_____

What is meant by the phrase "we shall be saved" in verse 9? _____

_____

Compare "justified by his blood" (5:9) with "justified by faith" (5:1). _____
Observe the reference to "joy" in 5:11. Compare this with "love" mentioned in 5:5. _____

_____

3. Read 5:12-21. In reading this longer paragraph, you may want to follow the intent of the parentheses in the Authorized Version enclosing verses 13-17. If that is followed, then the word "therefore" of verse 18 picks up the line of thought introduced by "wherefore" in verse 12.
What problem concerning justice appears in verse 19a?

_____

_____

What is your answer to this? _____
Compare the last phrase of verse 12 for help in answering the problem.
Underline in your Bible the words "grace" and "gift."

What is your definition of grace? _____

_____

What is a gift? _____

Does a gift benefit the receiver if it is not accepted by him? Apply this to the gift of God's Son to the world. ____

_____

Who are the two men of this paragraph? _____
Make a study of the various contrasts of this paragraph. Record your findings on Chart L.

CONTRASTS OF 5:12-21   Chart L

	Condemnation	Justification
Source (person)		
Extent		
Cause		
Nature		
Measure		
Result		

4. Write a list of the fruits of justification which you have observed in verses 6-21. _____

_____

_____

_____

III. COMMENTS.

The fruits or results of justification which accrue to the believer are identified throughout this chapter. These are those listed in verses 1-11:

A. Peace with God (5:1).

Through Christ judicial peace has been declared between God and the believer. Christ's work on the cross has paid our debt and settled all the claims against us.

B. Access into This Grace (5:2).
One who seeks an audience with a king must have right of access. Such access is given the believer by Jesus Christ.

C. Rejoicing in the Hope of the Glory of God (5:2).
For more light on this subject, read Romans 8:17-23; Philippians 3:20-21; I Peter 1:3-7; I John 3:2.

D. Rejoicing in Tribulations (5:3).
Rejoicing in such experiences is not natural to the human heart, but it may be found in the heart of one who has been justified. Such a believer knows that the very purpose of his trials is to produce patience, refined character and a hope that does not let one down. Read Acts 7:54-58 to see an example of a justified person having the love of God shed abroad in his heart by the Holy Spirit and being able to rejoice in tribulation.

E. Assurance of Future Deliverance (5:9-10).
We as believers are assured that if God's love was so great that He gave Christ to die for us while we were yet sinners, surely now that we are reconciled to Him and have become His children, we shall be safe in the future. The phrase "saved by his life" (5:10) refers to Christ's resurrected life. We are saved by His life because He is our life (read Col. 3:4).

F. Joy of Reconciliation (5:11).
In this verse the word "atonement" should be read as "reconciliation" (cf. "reconciled" of v. 10). Reconciliation is restoration to favor and harmony. This was Paul's thought in the opening verse of chapter 5, when he talked of "peace with God" (5:1). There is no greater cause for joy than this.

*　　*　　*

In the last paragraph (5:12-21) the spotlight is on the *free gift* of God, by contrasting it with death brought about by sin.

A question often asked about Adam's sin is Why should the whole human race be guilty for a sin which one man committed? Consider the following in answering this question:

1. Adam, the father of all people, was the embodiment of all mankind. The human race not only began with Adam, it was potentially a part of Adam. This may be called the solidarity of the human race. "Adam was both the individual and the race. His posterity are looked upon as acting with him because they are *his* posterity."* The Bible's teaching concerning an inherited sin nature would be false if the *unity* of the human race were not a fact.

2. When Adam sinned, all sinned (cf. 5:12). This is because of the solidarity of the human race. Sin entered the human race through *one* man, but all were involved.

3. Death for sin is thus the penalty for all mankind. In these ten verses (5:12-21) is set forth what may be called the doctrine of the two men, Adam the first and Adam the second. Or, the two headships, Adam and Christ. The first Adam stands as the federal head of the *old* creation, as seen in Genesis 1-2; and the second Adam is the Head of the *new* creation, as seen in Ephesians 1:19-23; 2:10 and II Corinthians 5:17. See Chart M showing the two headships.

THE TWO HEADSHIPS   Chart M

Sin and Salvation Seen in Their Sources   Romans 5:12, 18

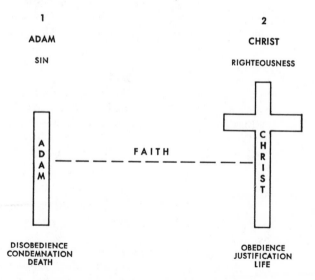

*Charles F. Pfeiffer and Everett F. Harrison (eds.), *The Wycliffe Bible Commentary*, p. 1198.

Verse 14 states that Adam is a figure or type of Christ. Adam was the federal head of the human race. We are all children of Adam and partakers of his human, sinful nature. Christ is the federal Head of a *new* race composed of believers who partake of His divine nature. Any child of Adam may by simple faith be identified with the new race of Christ. Faith is the only bridge by which one may come into this new relationship.

Verses 14 and 17 speak of the reign of death. The reign of sin and death over the old creation in the world is universal and absolute. But we who are in Christ are a new creation, and that reign of sin and death is broken for us by Christ. We shall reign in *life* (v. 17).

The last two verses of the chapter speak of the triumph of grace over sin. The function of the law is, as stated in verse 20, to reveal sin in all its hideousness. "The Ten Commandments were given so that all could see the extent of their failure to obey God's laws" (5:20, Living Letters). But Paul here shows that where sin most fully manifests itself grace abounds exceedingly beyond it. "And so sin ruled over all men and brought them to death, but now God's kindness rules instead, giving us right standing with God and resulting in eternal life through Jesus Christ our Lord" (5:21, Living Letters).

IV. SUMMARY.

The fruits of justification are manifold. Reconciliation, eternal life, joy and love are among the cherished gifts of God to His people.

Below are given the cores of the opening sentences of each of the three paragraphs of chapter 5. With these as a starter, see how much you can recall of the contents of each paragraph.

5:1-5: "Therefore . . . we have peace with God."

5:6-11: "For . . . Christ died."

5:12-21: "Wherefore . . . the free gift came upon all men."

Principles
of Christian Living

THIS LESSON BEGINS SECTION THREE

OF PAUL'S EPISTLE, WHERE HE WRITES

ON HOW TO LIVE THE CHRISTIAN LIFE.

Review survey Chart D, observing especially the outlines given for chapters 1-8. The easiest outline to remember for these chapters is the triplet Sin—Salvation—Sanctification. The progression of Paul's discussion is very logical. First he writes about sin: God's Holiness in Condemning Sin (1:18—3:20). That identifies the *need* of salvation. Then he writes about the offer and *way* of salvation: God's Grace in Justifying Sinners (3:21—4:25). His next subject is a natural sequel—how a saved person can live the Christian life. This is sanctification: God's Power in Sanctifying Believers (5:1—8:39).

The three sections may also be compared as shown in Chart N.

SIN—SALVATION—SANCTIFICATION

Chart N

1:18	3:21	5:1
No righteousness in us	God's righteousness on us	God's righteousness in us
God as Judge	Christ as Saviour	Holy Spirit as Sanctifier

(8:39 appears at the top right of the third column)

I. THE DOCTRINE OF SANCTIFICATION.

Some Christians avoid the word "sanctification" because it appears to suggest a mystical experience reserved for only a select few. Actually the doctrine of sanctification is one of the most practical and vital doctrines involving *every* believer. Sanctification is a work of God which begins in a Christian's life the moment he is saved. As a progressive experience it continues throughout his life and is completed when the Christian sees his Lord face to face and is made like Him (I John 3:2). Sanctification involves the negative *separation* from evil, and the positive *setting apart* for God's worship and service. For you as a Christian there are past, present and future aspects of sanctification, as shown in Chart O.°

PAST, PRESENT AND FUTURE ASPECTS OF SANCTIFICATION   Chart O

Past Aspect of Sanctification	Present Aspect of Sanctification	Future Aspect of Sanctification
Positional (1 Cor 1:2, 30). All believers were so sanctified as saints, the youngest as well as the oldest, the most carnal as well as the most spiritual.	Experiential. Depends upon our knowledge of and faith in our position in Christ (Rom 6:1-11), converting our position into experience.	Final. When we see the Lord and are made like Him—sinless, sickless, deathless (1 Cor 4; 15:54; 1 Jn 3:2).
Static, unalterable, inseparable from justification, and the result solely of our union with Christ.	Progressive, changeable, depends upon yieldedness to God's will (Rom 6:13) and conformity to God's Word (Rom 12:2). [Cf. John 17:17; II Cor. 3:18; I Thess. 5:23-24.]	Eternal [perfect]. Will result in our final state in eternity (Phil 3:21).
As God sees us in Christ (1 Cor 1:2, 30, with Phil. 1:1, etc.).	As we are in our conduct (2 Thess. 2:13).	As we shall be in glory (Rom 8:29; 1 Cor 15:49; [Eph. 5: 27]).

II. SURVEY OF 6:1—8:39.

Chapters 6-8 of Romans are thus chapters about victorious Christian living. For study, the section may be divided into three parts, as shown on Chart P.

VICTORIOUS CHRISTIAN LIVING   (ROMANS 6-8)   Chart P

	6:1 PRINCIPLES	7:7 PRACTICE	8:1 POWER 8:39
a key subject	surrender	self	Spirit

The first segment, 6:1—7:6, is the text studied in this lesson. Its subject is The Principles of Christian Living. The questions of how to live the Christian life must always·

°Chart from Merrill F. Unger, *Unger's Bible Handbook,* p. 615.

be answered by reference to sound principles and foundations. This segment teaches three such principles.

III. PARAGRAPH DIVISIONS.

At verses 6:1, 12; 7:1.

IV. ANALYSIS.

Before reading the segment of 6:1—7:6, mark dividing points in your Bible at 6:12 and 7:1. This divides the segment into three main parts.

As you read this passage, be on the lookout for reasons and motivations of Christian behavior. After your first reading, record some of your observations.

Three principles of Christian living are especially discussed in this passage: double identification, new servitude and total liberation. Record observations about these on Chart Q. Suggestions for study are given below.

PRINCIPLES OF CHRISTIAN LIVING   Chart Q

1 DOUBLE IDENTIFICATION	2 NEW SERVITUDE	3 TOTAL LIBERATION
6:1 (dead and alive)	6:12 (before and after)	7:1 (old and new)
6:11	6:23	7:6

A. Double Identification (6:1-11).

Note the repeated phrase "with him" in this paragraph. In what two ways is the Christian identified with Christ?

_____

What is the impact of the words "know" and "reckon" in this paragraph? _____

_____

Record these words on Chart Q. List all the things said about sin in the paragraph. How is the Christian's identification with Christ in death a solution to the problem of sin? _____

_____

_____

B. New Servitude (6:12-23).

Read these verses again and make a note of key repeated words. Such words usually give a clue as to the main intent of a passage. Observe that this middle part of the segment has strong command and exhortation. What is the key command word here? Record on Chart Q. What was the Christian's servitude before his conversion?_____

_____

What is it since his conversion?_____

_____

What wonderful truth does 6:14 teach? _____

_____

How is Romans 6:23 related to the verses preceding it? For your answer, consider the word "wages." Compare this word with "gift." _____

_____

_____

C. Total Liberation (7:1-6).

What is the opening word of these verses? _____
Compare this with the first paragraph. What key words
are repeated in 7:1-6? _____

_____

Observe such phrases as "loosed from," "free from," "de-
livered from." From what has the Christian been liberated?

_____

What are the contrasts of the paragraph? _____

_____

_____

D. Spiritual Truths (6:1—7:6).

Write a list of ten important spiritual truths taught by
this passage. _____

_____

_____

_____

_____

V. COMMENTS.

Three words used by Paul in this passage suggest some
of the basic principles involved in practical Christian living. The words are "know," "reckon" and "yield."

A. Know.

The believer's thoughts, words and actions should be
steered by what he knows, or should know, concerning his
own relationship to Christ and the law, such as:

1. THE OLD MAN IS CRUCIFIED WITH CHRIST (6:6). The
question asked in 6:1 was raised by the statements of
5:20-21, where Paul states that where sin most fully manifests itself, there grace abounds more exceedingly beyond
it. But, lest anyone should think that this would warrant
him to continue in sin in order to give God occasion to

show more and more of His grace, Paul hastens to explain that those who have come into Christ have, in their identification with Him, *died* to sin. "We believers were raised up in the risen Christ into a *new sphere of being*." We do not belong to the old creation and the realm of sin (6:2-4).

2. BEING RAISED WITH CHRIST BRINGS NEWNESS OF LIFE (6:4). The one who by his faith is identified with Christ is, in God's sight and in God's reckoning, identified with *all* Christ's experiences, which include His resurrection as well as His death. Being resurrected with Him, the Christian lives unto God (6:10).

3. REGENERATION BRINGS DELIVERANCE FROM THE BOND-AGE OF THE LAW (7:6). As Christians we are no longer in the realm where stern law is constantly making demands upon us, but we have passed out into the realm where God is our Father, not our judge. We are free children of God, living now not merely to try to keep a law, but living to try to please our heavenly Father. Although Paul here makes it clear that Christians are *freed* from the law's bondage, he hastens to explain in the next verses (7:7 ff.) that the law is not an unholy thing. The law is holy, just and good (7:12), but we can never be made holy by the law because the office of the law is not to cleanse from sin but to show that there *is* sin from which to be cleansed, as the apostle himself had found (7:7).

B. Reckon.

The word translated "reckon" in the Authorized Version is translated in other versions by such words as "consider," "count," "regard," "think," "look upon." In this context reckoning goes one step further than knowing. As Christians we should know the facts stated in 6:1-10, count them as true and act accordingly. When sin tempts us, we should act as though we were indeed dead, giving absolutely no response to the temptation. But when God speaks we should act as though we were very much alive, giving absolute and instant obedience to Him. "Sin is described as the slave master who was in control of our former life; but since we died to sin, we are now declared to be liberated from this bondage,"† and we should regard ourselves as so

---

†Charles R. Erdman, *The Epistle of Paul to the Romans*, p. 71.

liberated. In so doing, of course, we are not presuming the attainment of sinless perfection. As Charles Erdman says, "Our evil passions and dispositions are still active and powerful. We must, however, disown their rule."[†]

C. Yield.

Christians are not under the death-dealing indictment of the law, but under the life-giving compulsion of grace (6:14-15). Paul makes it very clear that Christians are still bondslaves (servants, e.g., 6:18). But now they serve a new Master, to whom they must *yield* total allegiance and faithful service. This means throwing themselves upon God in full surrender to His will, constantly presenting each member of their being to Him as instruments of righteousness (6:13).

VI. SUMMARY.

The basic problem in Christian living is sins (the problem of sin having been settled once and for all for the Christian when he was saved). In Romans 6-8 Paul is talking about sins, and the temptations to commit sins which come to Christians daily. In 6:1—7:6 he lays down the principles which should govern Christians in their everyday walk. Three such principles are:

1. Double identification. The Christian is identified with Christ in death "unto sin" and resurrection "unto God."
2. New servitude. The Christian is now a bondslave of righteousness.
3. Total liberation. The Christian has been liberated from the "old" life (indictment of the law) to the "new" life (compulsion of the Spirit).

Let us conclude our study of this lesson by reading the wonderful words of 6:22: "*But now* being made free from sin, and become servants to God, *Ye have* your fruit unto holiness, and the end everlasting life."

---

† *Ibid.*, p. 72.

The Practice and Power of Christian Living

MANY CHRISTIANS ARE IN THE WORLD TODAY, BUT UNFORTUNATELY THEIR INFLUENCE IS NOT WHAT IT SHOULD BE.

As one has said, "The need of the world is that a great company of people so live that they will remind others of the Lord Jesus." Christianity as a force and witness is what Christians are individually, and Christians are individually what measure of victory is theirs in "performing that which is good" (7:18). Because the old nature still resides in a Christian, the problem of sins continually asserts itself. Where is the Christian's victory in the conflict between the old and new natures? How can he perform that which is good? Paul, inspired of the Holy Spirit, answers this question in the Bible text of this lesson.

Many Christians who have seen clearly and accepted God's method of deliverance from the guilt of sin have never seen clearly nor accepted God's method of deliverance from the power of sin. As you study this lesson let it be your earnest prayer that deliverance from the power of sin, spoken of in these verses, may be your daily experience.

As was shown in the last lesson, the subject of Romans 6:1—8:39 is Victorious Christian Living. Recall the outline shown in Chart R.

EXCERPT FROM CHART P   Chart R

6:1	7:7	8:1	8:39
PRINCIPLES	PRACTICE	POWER	

In the last lesson we learned about the principles. In this lesson our study centers on practice and power.

I. PARAGRAPH DIVISIONS.

Practice (7:7-25): at verses 7, 14.
Power (8:1-39): at verses 1, 9, 12, 18, 26, 28, 31.

II. ANALYSIS.

A. Practice (7:7-25).
In the practice of everyday living, the problem of Christians is how to perform that which is good (7:18). Keep this subject in mind as you read these verses. What key

words appear throughout the passage? _____

_____

_____

Make a special study of these two words:
   1. LAW. Observe the occurrences of "the law" (also "the commandment"). Compare this with "a law" (v. 21), "another law," "the law of my mind," "the law of sin" (vv. 23, 25).
   2. SIN. The word is singular throughout the passage. But in which paragraph are individual acts of sin, or sins,

predominant? _____
How does this observation parallel your observation above

concerning the word "law"? _____

1. Read 7:7-13 again. This paragraph might have been included with the preceding section (6:1—7:7) because it speaks of the principle of law. But it is rightly included in this new section on practice because it is the backdrop to the whole problem of sins in the Christian's experience. What is taught in this paragraph about the law of God?

_____

_____

In your own words, how is the law of God holy and good?

_____

_____

2. Read 7:14-25. The conflict described in these verses is the conflict going on inside the heart of a Christian. What

expressions characterize a Christian under the control of sin? _____

_____

What expressions speak of a Christian under the control of Christ? _____

_____

_____

Observe that the problem stated as a "how?" in verse 18 becomes one stated as a "who?" in verse 24. What is Paul's answer to the problem? _____

_____

What is implied in the brief answer of 25a? _____

_____

B. Power (8:1-39).

This chapter may be studied in various ways. For example, try making a topical study, and record below all that is taught concerning the three Persons of the Trinity:

Father (referred to in the text as "God"): _____

_____

_____

_____

Son: _____

_____

_____

Holy Spirit (Rom. 8 is a key chapter in the Bible on the Holy Spirit): _____

_____

_____

_____

For the remainder of your analysis, record your different observations on the analytical Chart S. Look for general things first, such as the main point of each paragraph; then analyze the smaller details.

Your main study should center about the subject "More Than Conquerors" (cf. 8:37). This is the main contribution of Romans 8—telling how the Christian can live a victorious Christian life, when the conflict of 7:14-25 rages continually within him. As you read the Bible text, underline every phrase that reveals any kind of help given the Christian to walk pleasing to God. Record on analytical Chart S, opposite each paragraph box, the different truths taught in the chapter concerning the Spirit-filled life.

1. In your study observe also that with Paul the overcoming life is not a mediocre existence, barely winning in the conflicts. Go through the entire chapter again and note all the strong words and phrases suggesting a full, abundant, invincible life (e.g., "freely give us all things," v. 32).

2. Recall that Paul had said earlier that the answer to the problem of the conflict within him (7:14-25) was to be found in "Jesus Christ our Lord" (7:25). Yet throughout chapter 8 emphasis is on the help of the Holy Spirit. How do you account for this? (Cf. 8:1.) _____

_____

3. Compare the first and last verses of chapter 8. _____

_____

4. See 8:28-30. Verse 28 may be read as "And we know that God causes all things to work together for good to those who love God . . ." (NASB). What is the one main impression you get from this paragraph? _____

_____

What is the repeated pronoun? _____
Study the meaning of each verb, and the significance of these works of God for the believer. On the subject of calling, read II Thessalonians 2:13-14 and II Peter 1:10.

5. See 8:31-39. What are the various kinds of hardships and obstacles mentioned here? _____

_____

The Spirit-filled Life

1
9
12
18
26
28
31
39

The phrase translated "we are more than conquerors" means "we are in the process of winning." How is this an encouragement to the Christian for his *daily* living? _____

III. COMMENTS.

A. Practice (7:7-25).

When one believes on Jesus Christ as his Saviour, God not only blots out all his past sins but He also imparts to the believer His own divine nature. This is the "new birth" of which Jesus spoke to Nicodemus in John 3:3-7. The believer is now a child of God (Gal. 3:26). From this time forth he is a temple of God, the Spirit of God dwelling in him (I Cor. 3:16; 6:19), and the progressive process of being made anew into the likeness of his Creator begins.

The regenerate man is an absolutely new creature. Before the new birth he had but one nature; after the new birth he has two natures. Before the new birth he had only the old corrupt nature inherited from Adam; after the new birth he has also the new, divine, spiritual nature imparted by God.

This explains why, when one is regenerated, he immediately begins to love the things which he used to hate and hate the things that he used to love. He possesses a new nature, with its new tastes, new ambitions, new aims. He is a new creature (II Cor. 5:17).

The believer's two natures also account for the conflict which goes on within him when temptation comes. The old nature has for years had complete control of his members (mouth, hands, brain, eyes), using them as "instruments of unrighteousness" (Rom. 6:13), over which it is loathe to lose control. So, when the new, holy, divine nature is imparted and would use the Christian's members as "instruments of righteousness" (6:13), there is a conflict. This conflict is depicted in Romans 7:14-25. Paul explains, however, that the way to victory is through Jesus Christ the Lord (7:25).

B. Power (8:1-39).

When we reach chapter 8 of Romans and look back through the preceding chapters on all that God has done for us as believers in Christ up to this point, it seems that there is nothing more that could possibly be done for us. Saved from the just penalty of our sins, all our past transgressions forgiven and blotted out, a new nature imparted to us, made free from the bondage of sin and the law—what more is there for the Christian? More, much more, as this glorious chapter 8 reveals.

In this chapter we reach the very climax of the gospel message, the very highest peak in this mountain range of blessings, the summing up of all the past, present and future benefits which accrue to the one who trusts in the Lord Jesus Christ. Chapter 8 begins with "no condemnation" and ends with "no separation," while in between there is "no defeat." "No condemnation" and "no separation" refer to the Christian's standing; "no defeat" refers to his state.

Verse 4 shows that the great purpose of Christ's death was not merely to save sinners from the penalty of sin, but "that the righteousness of the law might be fulfilled in us"—that we who are saved by Christ might become Christlike. The very purpose of justification is sanctification.

God not only frees the believer from sin through the work of Christ on the cross, but He helps the believer have victory over sin by the indwelling Holy Spirit. Christ's death on the cross gives the believer freedom from the sin principle of condemnation (vv. 2-3), and the Holy Spirit's indwelling presence gives the believer freedom from the sin practice of bondage (vv. 11, 13). The indwelling Spirit enables the believer to "mortify the deeds of the body" (v. 13) or, as the Williams' version reads, to "put a stop to the doings of your lower nature."

Chapter 8 says much about what we are and have in Christ, as well as what help is given to us. For example, we are sons of God as well as children of God (vv. 14, 17, 21; cf. Gal. 4:1-7). Concerning adoption, C. I. Scofield's definition is "Adoption is the act of God whereby one already a child is, through redemption from the law, placed in the position of an adult son."

Romans 8:17 also declares we are "heirs of God, and joint-heirs with Christ." This is marvelous! The wealth to which we Christians are heirs is almost beyond comprehension. Read Hebrews 1:2; John 3:35; 13:3; 16:15; Acts 10:36; Ephesians 1:20-23, and note the expression "all things." And in Romans 8:32 and I Corinthians 3:21-23 we are told that God has given us in Christ "all things." The cattle on a thousand hills are His; He owns the wealth of sea and land; the sun, moon and innumerable stars of

73

the universe are His. And all these are as nothing, compared with spiritual riches such as joy, peace and love, of which we are also heirs.

Verses 18-25 give to the Christian the assurance of future glory. Into this glorious inheritance as sons of God we do not enter at once. Our Father wills that we as redeemed ones remain in these bodies for a while for our discipline and also for the work of witnessing. In these bodies there is much suffering to endure, but "the sufferings of this present time are not worthy to be compared with the glory which shall be revealed in us" (v. 18). We are to keep our thoughts not on the sufferings but on the glory to come.

In addition to all else that the Holy Spirit does He inspires prayer (vv. 26-27). Prayer is the highest form of Christian activity. It is absolutely essential to a successful Christian life. But we are weak and ignorant of what to pray for and how to pray. In this the Spirit helps our infirmities. "The Holy Spirit prays for us with such feeling that it cannot be expressed in words" (8:26b, Living Letters).

In I John 5:14-15 we are told that if we ask anything according to God's will, He hears, and we know that if He hears, we have the petition asked. So prayers inspired by the Holy Spirit, and consequently according to the will of God (8:27), will be heard and answered. Let us depend more on the Holy Spirit's help in our prayer life.

Verses 28-30 explain God's eternal purpose in Christ concerning believers. God is controlling all things, even the sufferings and hardships of life, for the development and ultimate good of those who love Him and whom He has called (v. 28). The ones referred to in verse 28 as "them that love God" and "them who are the called" are those who have responded to the call of God, not merely those who have been invited. God invites all; those who respond to the invitation are the called ones. He has called believers for a purpose and that purpose is stated in verse 29: that they might "be conformed to the image of his Son."

Notice in verse 30 the word "glorified" is in the past tense like the other verbs, as though the glorification of believers had already taken place. This is because, in the mind and purpose of God, the believer's glorification is already accomplished. "God sees us not only as we are, but as we shall be; with Him it is done; with us, experimentally, it is yet to be."

Can a Christian ask for any more assurance of eternal life than what is taught in Romans 8? As believers our hope is eternally secure because of Christ's work for us in the past (vv. 2-3); because of the Holy Spirit's work for us in the present (vv. 13-14, 16, 26-27); because of God's purpose and glorious plans for us for the future (vv. 18-23, 28-31); and because it is impossible for the believer to be separated from the love of Christ (vv. 35-39).

In verse 31 we see that God is "for" us who have accepted salvation in Christ. In verse 34 we see that Christ is for us, and in verse 26 we see that the Holy Spirit is for us. In everything, therefore, we are more than conquerors. Such are the concluding words of Paul in answering the original question of how to perform the good. Concerning the last verses of chapter 8, one commentator has remarked that the words "strike all thoughtful interpreters and readers as transcending almost everything in language."

IV. SUMMARY.

Inside the heart of a Christian a conflict between his old and new nature goes on daily. Victory is possible through Christ by the power of the Holy Spirit. Here then is a real test of the Christian's faith in God's promises, and of his obedience to God's Word. "We can obey God's laws if we follow after the Holy Spirit and no longer obey the old evil nature within us" (8:4, Living Letters). Victory today (8:1-17), glory to come (8:18-30) and fellowship with God forever (8:31-39) are the happy fruits of God's work of sanctification in the heart of the believer.

God's Sovereignty
in Saving Jew and Gentile

ANY FULL DISCUSSION OF SALVATION

MUST CONSIDER THE PAST, PRESENT

AND FUTURE OF THE JEWISH NATION.

This is necessary because Israel is the special object of divine attention for practically all of Old Testament history (beginning at Gen. 12) and for much of the New. Coupled with this is the fact of an indissoluble covenant which extends to the end of time which God made with Israel.

In chapters 9-11 of Romans Paul is writing especially about Israel and Gentiles as entities, not individuals. In chapters 1-8 he has discussed the salvation of individuals —Jew or Gentile. Now he can focus his attention on the salvation of the nation of true Israel by comparing it with the salvation of Gentiles.

You may want to study this lesson in smaller units because of the length of the passage involved. If so, it is recommended that it be divided into three parts according to the lesson's outline.

I. SURVEY OF 9:1—11:36.

A brief outline of this section of Romans is indicated on Chart T.

GOD'S SOVEREIGNTY IN SAVING JEW AND GENTILE   Chart T

9:1 INTRODUCTION	9:6 GOD'S SOVEREIGNTY	9:30　　　　10:21 MAN'S RESPONSIBILITY	11:1 GOD'S PURPOSE	11:30　　　　11:36 CONCLUSION
Paul's Concern for Israel	(over Jew and Gentile)	(Jew and Gentile)	for ISRAEL (related to Gentile)	God's Purpose for Mankind

Before analyzing any one segment, read the three chapters in one sitting with this outline before you, to see the general movement of Paul's exposition. Observe the following:

1. In the opening paragraph (9:1-5) Paul introduces the reader to his theme, by citing the problem of Israel's defection.

2. In the first and second main segments (9:6-29; 9:30—10:21) Paul discusses truths and principles applicable to both Jew and Gentile. God's sovereignty and man's responsibility are the two grand subjects involved.

3. With the above discussion as a background, Paul begins at 11:1 to talk particularly about Israel, and shows hopefully how their alienation will eventually be changed to restoration.

4. The concluding section (11:30-36) returns to the universal theme, showing God's purpose for all mankind. At the last verse, Paul has reached the peak: "For of him, and through him, and to him, are all things: to whom be glory for ever. Amen."

II. PARAGRAPH DIVISIONS.

Paragraph divisions are as follows (always mark divisions in your Bible before you begin to study):

A. Introduction (9:1-5, one paragraph).

B. God's Sovereignty (9:6-29).
At verses 6, 10, 14, 22.

C. Man's Responsibility (9:30—10:21).
At verses 9:30; 10:1, 4, 14, 16.

D. God's Purpose for Israel (11:1-27).
At verses 1, 7, 11, 13, 17, 25.

E. Conclusion (11:30-36).
At verses 30, 33.

III. ANALYSIS.

A. Introduction: Paul's Concern for Israel (9:1-5).

1. What is revealed about Paul here? _____

_____

2. Explain what is meant by each of the Jews' advantages cited in this paragraph. Consult the related verses listed below.

a. "the adoption" (Exodus 4:22; Deut. 14:1; Hosea 11:1)

_____

b. "the glory" (Exodus 25:8, 21-22; 40:34-35; I Kings 8:11) _____

_____

c. "the covenants" (e.g., Abrahamic: Gen. 12:1-3; 15:18; Mosaic: Exodus 19:3-25; 20:1-26; Davidic: II Sam. 7:16; I Chron. 17:7) _____

_____

d. "the law" (Exodus 19:16—20:1) _____

e. "the service" (ritual of the tabernacle and temple: Heb. 9—10) _____

_____

f. "the promises" (especially Messianic: e.g., Isa. 52:13—53:12) _____

_____

g. "the fathers" (name the major patriarchs) _____

_____

h. "Christ"—the supreme distinction _____

_____

B. God's Sovereignty (9:6-29).

This segment deals with God's sovereign choices of vessels for salvation and service, whether they are of Jewish or non-Jewish origin. The doctrine of sovereign election challenges the keenest of minds to fathom its depths. In this passage Paul answers questions brought to him concerning it (e.g., see v. 14). Sometimes when Paul answers such questions, he does not attempt a logical explanation; consistently he rests in what the Scripture says. If we are honest believers we will recognize that the truth of a biblical doctrine does not depend on the human mind's comprehension of it. "We must let certain Scriptures lie just as they are, whether or not they consort with our conceptions, or whether we find ourselves able to 'reconcile' them with our 'theological system' or not."*

Study this passage especially to see its prominent truths. Sound interpretative procedure is to let the prominent and clear texts control the interpretation of the difficult or obscure texts.

1. Observe how God is the sovereign Actor throughout the passage. Would God be God if He were not sovereign?

Note the illustration of verses 20-21. _____

2. Two examples of God's sovereign election of true Israel are given in the first two paragraphs (vv. 6-9; 10-13). Although Abraham was the father of Israel, not all descendants of Abraham are true Israel. Abraham had more than one son, but only through Isaac would his seed be perpetuated (9:7). Isaac had more than one son, but it was Jacob who was called (9:13). What does verse 11 teach about the purpose of God which operates by selec-

tion? _____

_____

3. According to verse 14, what basic attribute of God must

be recognized for any sound view of His sovereignty? ____

_____

Why is this basic? _____

4. History illustrates divine sovereignty. Observe how Paul brings this out through such words as "show" and "de-

*William R. Newell, *Romans Verse by Verse*, p. 373.

clare" in verses 17-23. What attributes of God are thus revealed? _____

5. Where in this segment does Paul write that sovereign election refers to Gentiles as well as Jews? Study the context of the verse. _____

6. What is taught about a remnant of Israel in verse 27?

_____

C. Man's Responsibility (9:30—10:21).

In the previous segment God is the main Actor throughout. As the Sovereign, God initiates and completes His redemptive work in the hearts of those He calls. In the present segment people are the subject of the action, the action being response to the glad tidings of salvation. In both segments, Jews and Gentiles are involved, with particular attention given to Jews.

MAN'S RESPONSIBILITY   (9:30—10:21)   Chart U

TWO DIFFERENT RESPONSES	Israel's Refusal To SUBMIT	INVITATION TO ALL		Israel's Refusal To OBEY	
		Content of Invitation	Hearers of Invitation		
9:30 GENTILES: ISRAEL:	10:1	10:4	10:14	10:16	10:21
	ZEAL, but NO SUBMISSION			KNOWLEDGE, but NO OBEDIENCE	

In connection with this dual truth of God's sovereign action and man's opportunity to respond, A. Berkeley Mickelsen writes:

> If a teacher minimizes either of these two aspects—God's action or the believer's response—he has departed from the NT. If one thinks that he fully understands the relation between these two factors, he has forgotten that God has left some things to be revealed in the ages to come (cf. Eph 2:7).†

As you read the segment paragraph by paragraph, follow the general outline given on Chart U. Then continue your analysis of each paragraph, and record key words, phrases and outlines in the spaces provided. After you have worked with this for a while, you will begin to see why Paul's heart was so heavy for his brethren the Jews. Observe what this passage teaches about the following subjects:

1. how a Gentile is saved
2. a major stumbling stone for the Jew
3. zeal of the Jew
4. righteousness attained through the law (10:5)
5. conditions for salvation: confession and faith
6. universality of the gospel
7. broadcast of the gospel
8. responsibility and accountability according to light
9. the burden of a man's heart for his people's salvation

D. God's Purpose for Israel (11:1-29).

Now Paul looks to the future of Israel as it is related to Gentile destiny.

> Blended together in a sublime picture are the scope of history, the attitudes and response of Israel and the Gentiles, and the wisdom of God in the inter-relations of these two groups.‡

In chapters 9—11, when writing about the Jews, Paul moves in the direction, chronologically speaking, shown on Chart V.

†A. Berkeley Mickelsen in *Wycliffe Bible Commentary*, Charles F. Pfeiffer and Everett F. Harrison (eds.), p. 1218.

‡*Wycliffe Bible Commentary*, p. 1216.

PAUL WRITES ABOUT THE JEWS Chart V

PAST ⟶	PRESENT ⟶	FUTURE
(Israel Selected) (9:6-29)	(Israel Rejected) (9:30—10:21)	(Israel Accepted) (11:1-29)

There is also a progression in the expression of Paul's feelings for Israel at these three junctions in this section:
1. Heaviness—"great heaviness and continual sorrow" (9:2).
2. Desire—"My heart's desire and prayer to God for Israel is, that they might be saved" (10:1).
3. Hope—"God hath not cast away his people" (11:2).
The atmosphere of bright hope pervades the verses of the passage now to be studied.

Analyze this segment as you did the previous one, reading the paragraphs in connection with Chart W, and recording your own observations.

GOD'S PURPOSE FOR ISRAEL (11:1-29) Chart W

Remnant Preserved		Present Purposes and Future Prospects of Israel's Alienation			Ultimate Restoration	
11:1	11:7	11:11	11:13	11:17	11:25	11:29
Remnant and grace	Nonremnant and darkness	Gentiles' fullness	Gentiles' _____	Gentiles' _____		
		"How much more"				
		Jews' _____	Jews' _____	Jews' _____		

82

1. List the truths taught about the Jewish remnant in the first two paragraphs. Was there a remnant existing in Paul's day? If so, then it may be accepted as true that the Jews' national rejection of Jesus at Calvary did not erase the fact of a continuing remnant, because Calvary took place before Paul wrote Romans 11:5.

2. What is the common theme of the three paragraphs in 11:11-24? _____

_____

Observe the repetition of the phrase "how much more." Fill in words as indicated on Chart W. What is Paul's point in all of this? _____

_____

_____

3. List the important truths taught by the last paragraph. What is meant by "the fulness of the Gentiles be come in"? Consult a commentary for help. How inclusive is the phrase "All Israel shall be saved"? When will all this take place? _____

_____

4. Read 11:29 as "God does not revoke His free gifts or the call by which He makes His people His own."§

E. Conclusion: God's Purpose for Mankind (11:30-36).

Paul concludes his discussion of God's sovereign ways with Jews and non-Jews on a high note of adoration and praise of God.

1. Read 11:30-32. What is the key word of this paragraph?

_____

Relate the phrase "mercy upon all" (v. 32) to all that Paul has written about Jew and Gentile. Compare the reading of verse 32 in various modern versions.

2. Read 11:33-36. What attributes of God are recognized here? _____

_____

_____

§F. F. Bruce, *The Letters of Paul*, p. 223.

How does each relate to the subject of chapters 9—11?

_____

Read Isaiah 40:13 and Job 41:11 for background of verses
34–35. In your own words, make an expanded paraphrase
of verse 36. _____

3. Think back over the content of chapters 9—11, and write
a list of ten spiritual truths taught in this section. _____

_____

_____

_____

_____

_____

IV. COMMENTS.

The miracle of Israel today is that four thousand years
after its birth, with most of its life having been spent in
disobedience to God, the nation even exists. The tragedy
of Israel has been the divine judgment of its scattering
throughout the world. The climax of Israel's disobedience
and rebellion was in their rejection of Jesus as their Messiah. For this, God set them aside. But a restoration of
Israel is foretold by Scripture (cf. Rom. 11:26), so that a
scattered people will one day be united in their own land
of promise. The formation of a new state of Israel in 1948
and the continuing occupation of much of Palestine by
Jews returning from all parts of the world points to a future spiritual restoration of Israel, when they will recognize Jesus Christ as their long-sought Messiah and will,
as a nation, be accepted by Him.

A. Introduction: Paul's Concern for Israel (9:1-5).
Paul thinks over all the mighty favors which have been
granted to Israel, and sadly contemplates the fact that
in spite of them his people are without the blessedness

enjoyed by Christian believers, of which blessedness he has been writing with such rapture in chapter 8. The Jews' "supreme privilege and distinction is this, that from them has come Christ, of their own blood so far as His assumed humanity is concerned, but in his eternal 'being' 'over all, God blessed for ever.' "‖

B. God's Sovereignty (9:6-29).

Divine sovereignty has been defined simply as God's freedom of action. All creatures, because all are sinners, justly deserve the wrath of God. In His mercy God has predestined some of these to salvation. It is His liberty to dispense His blessings where and how He pleases (cf. Eph. 1:5, 9, 11). He does not explain why He chooses some over others.

The hardening of Pharaoh's heart is a stumbling block to many people. In the account in Exodus these three statements are made: (1) that God hardened Pharaoh's heart (Exodus 7:13); (2) that Pharaoh's heart was hardened (Exodus 8:19); and (3) that Pharaoh hardened his own heart (Exodus (8:15). God's messages and judgments were not the cause but the occasion of the hardening of Pharaoh's heart. The same messages and judgments which hardened Pharaoh's heart caused some of his servants to yield to God.

If human beings could only faintly comprehend the immeasurable distance between the greatness of God and their own insignificance, they would not have the colossal impertinence to question God's ways or will, or demand that He explain Himself. They would bow to the truth of the sovereignty of God without question.

> Indeed, as creatures of God, men could hardly sit in judgment upon God and accuse him of injustice if he had been arbitrary and capricious and severe; but how can anyone accuse God of injustice in view of the way he actually has dealt with men? He has been patient and long-suffering toward his impenitent people, Israel, and has purposed to show all the wealth of his glory toward the objects of his mercy, chosen not only from among the Jews, his covenant people, but even from among the Gentiles . . . Vs. 19-24.#

‖ Charles R. Erdman, *The Epistle of Paul to the Romans,* p. 103.

#*Ibid.,* p. 109.

C. Man's Responsibility (9:30—10:21).

In the previous segment the truth of God's sovereignty with respect to man's salvation is taught. In this segment is emphasized the truth of man's freedom to accept or reject God's way.

The question is often asked, Which is true, God's sovereignty or man's free will? They are both true. They are both taught in the Word of God. We are to believe them both. The two truths do not conflict and would not seem contradictory if we could see, as God sees, the end from the beginning. If they seem to human intellect to be contradictory it is because human intellect is incapable of fully understanding God's thoughts and ways (see Rom. 11:33).

In speaking of these two great truths a preacher once gave this illustration: A man walking along the highway comes suddenly to a great, magnificent building and sees written over the doorway "Whosoever will may enter here." The man considers a while and then decides to enter. The first thing that meets his eye as he steps inside is his own name written on the wall, and beneath it the words "Chosen before the foundation of the world." Let us apply the illustration to our subject. Man hears the gospel message and the invitation "Whosoever will may come." He is perfectly free to accept or reject. He decides to accept the invitation and finds himself "in Christ." Then it is that he learns that God has chosen him before the foundation of the world (Eph. 1:4).

Paul writes of two contrasting kinds of righteousness. The righteousness which is of the law is one of *doing* something. The righteousness which is of faith is one of *trusting* in something which has been done. It is trusting in the finished work of Christ. The contrast is between salvation by works and salvation by faith. The first is impossible for any; the second is possible for all.

The righteousness which is by faith does not ask that anything be done. It does not ask who shall ascend to heaven to bring Christ down (v. 6): Christ has already come down to earth in human form. Neither does it ask who shall descend into the deep to bring up Christ again from the dead (v. 7): Christ has already been brought again from the dead. It is simply "the word of faith" that brings salvation (v. 8). It is a word of confession that Jesus is Lord, which is the result of heart belief in His finished work (vv. 9-10). Of course, a heart belief that Christ has done all that is necessary to be done, and a confession of this fact, means an absolute abandonment of all the "works way" of salvation and a complete surrender to "the faith way" of salvation which is God's way.

Paul makes the great point that although Israel as a nation is rejected at the present time, any individual Israelite (or all Israelites, if they will) may, by simply believing in Christ, enter into a far greater degree of favor with God than was ever offered to the nation in the past.

God is not dealing unjustly with the Israelites. He is offering to them, as well as to the Gentiles, all the riches of heaven in Christ. The only reason Israel continues to be rejected of God is because they will not accept these blessings in Christ. Jesus is to the majority of the Israelites a stumbling stone and rock of offense (9:33).

D. God's Purpose for Israel (11:1-29).

God has not finished His dealings with Israel. Their present rejection is neither total nor final. Their rejection is not total because, even in this present time of national rejection, any individual Israelite who will believe on Christ is accepted of God. And Israel's rejection is not final because there is a time coming in the future when Israel as a nation will accept Christ and therefore be accepted of God.

1. ISRAEL'S REJECTION NOT TOTAL (11:1-10). This chapter opens with a question which many people are asking today, "Hath God cast away His people [forever]?" Has God ended His dealings with Israel? Is the glorious history of this ancient nation over? Is Israel utterly and finally rejected of God?

Paul emphatically denies that such is the case (v. 1). No individual Israelite is rejected now if he will come into God's favor in the one appointed way, through faith in Christ. And ultimately all national Israel shall be saved and any glory of their past history will be as nothing to that which is to come.

To prove that individual Israelites can be accepted of God in this present age, the apostle points to his own case (v. 1). He is an Israelite and he is surely not rejected of God. On the contrary, God has appointed him to a very responsible position, making him the apostle of the Gentiles (v. 13), to carry the news of salvation to them. And there are many Jews besides himself, Paul points out, who are accepted of God. It might seem as though all Israelites were rejected and only Gentiles were being accepted, because so many more Gentiles than Jews were accepting Christ in Paul's time. But Paul reminds his readers of a similar situation in Elijah's day (vv. 2-6).

There has been a remnant of believers throughout the history of Israel, though not always discernible nor accurately measured. Examples are:

    a. in Elijah's time (I Kings 19:18)
    b. in Isaiah's time (Isa. 1:9)
    c. during captivity (e.g., Ezekiel, Daniel, Shadrach, Meshach, Abednego)
    d. during restoration (Ezra, Nehemiah and followers)
    e. at the time of Jesus' birth (e.g., John the Baptist, Simeon, Anna; Luke 2:38)
    f. during the church age (Rom. 11:4-5)

2. ISRAEL'S REJECTION NOT FINAL (11:11-32) The question asked in verse 11 is equivalent to asking, Have they stumbled beyond recovery? Is the condition of Israel incurable? Although individual Israelites are being saved, how about national Israel? Is Israel's national rejection final? Paul's emphatic "God forbid" denies the possibility of such a tragedy.

> That there is to be such a national restoration of the Jews, Paul argues from their actual relationship to God. He employs two figures of speech. The "firstfruit" which is offered to God makes holy the entire mass from which it is taken; it indicates that the whole belongs to God. So, too, the root of a tree gives life and character to the branches, and "if the root is holy, so are the branches." Vs. 11-16.
> Thus it is with Israel . . . they will yet appear in their real character and will manifest that relation to God which is theirs by right, and is in accordance with his changeless purpose.**

Partial blindness of Israel will persist until "the fulness of the Gentiles be come in" (11:25). This latter phrase

**Ibid., pp. 124-25.

may be read "until the full number of the Gentiles enters in" (cf. Acts 15:14-17). According to 11:25-26 Israel's blindness and ungodliness will end with the coming of Israel's Deliverer, for that is God's covenant with them. Chart X shows that we are now living in the church age, and that the second coming of Christ will herald the end of this Gentile era.

ISRAEL IN RELATION TO THE CHURCH AGE Chart X

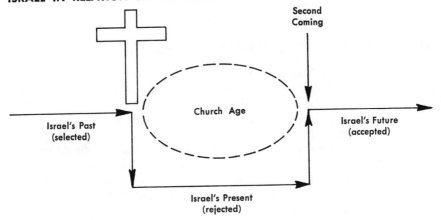

V. CONCLUSION.

> O the unfathomable abundance of God's wisdom and knowledge! How unsearchable are His decrees! How inscrutable His ways! As the prophet says:
> > Who has understood the mind of the Lord?
> > Or who has shared His counsel?
> > Who has first given to Him,
> > > That he should be repaid his gift?
> > For all things proceed from Him, exist through Him, and return to Him: to Him be the glory throughout all ages. Amen.††

With this burst of praise from the apostle's heart, the doctrinal section of his epistle comes to a close. Paul will teach more doctrine in the succeeding chapters, but his main burden will be the application of doctrine to Christian service.

††Rom. 11:33-36, Bruce, p. 223.

The Christian Servant

THIS LESSON BEGINS THE DIVISION OF

ROMANS ENTITLED 'PRACTICAL,' WITH

EMPHASIS ON ONE'S EVERYDAY CONDUCT.

Paul, having set forth in the preceding chapters the great doctrines of Christianity, proceeds now to tell Christians how they are to conduct themselves in every walk of life to the glory of God. "Paul always bases duty upon doctrine; he traces life to belief; he shows that character is determined by creed."[*] Doctrine and practice should never be divorced from each other. Mere head knowledge of doctrine is cold and lifeless. Actually the full orb of Christian responsibility regarding the truths of Scripture is threefold:

LEARN THE TRUTHS
APPROPRIATE THE TRUTHS
LIVE THE TRUTHS
("Hear the word . . . receive it . . . bring forth fruit,"
Mark 4:20)

In your studies of these chapters of Romans consider yourself to be the one *particular* person addressed by Paul: "I beseech you therefore." Paul of course wrote to a group of Christians, but the Holy Spirit's particular intent was that *you*, with others, live the truths of these chapters.

Review survey Chart D. Note the complete outline which leads up to this: God's Glory the Object of Service. All Christian service should have as its goal the glory of God. Review the other outlines of the chart, observing especially the different identifications given to this practical division of 12:1—15:13.

---

[*]Charles R. Erdman, *The Epistle of Paul to the Romans*, p. 131.

I. SURVEY OF 12:1—15:13.

For these next three lessons our study will center on this last major division of Romans, 12:1—15:13. For a survey view, make a cursory reading of this passage as you follow Chart Y.

PRACTICAL CHRISTIAN SERVICE

12:1	12:3	12:9 12:21	13:1	13:8	13:11 13:14	14:1				15:8 15:13
	Christian Servant		Christian Citizen			Christian Brother				
						Christian's Position on Questioned Practices				
							14:13	15:1		
Introduction	Gifts for Service	Obligations to Others	Subjection to Authorities	Attitude of Love	Armor of Light	Principle of Liberty (tolerance)	Principle of Love (care)	Example of Christ (obedience)	Conclusion	
Consecration of Christian									Glory of God	
	Lesson 11		Lesson 12			Lesson 13				

1. Which parts of this outline stress something *given* to the Christian (e.g., gifts, 12:3-8)? _____

_____

2. Compare the introduction and the conclusion. _____

_____

3. Which parts of the outline stress the Christian's relation to others? _____

_____

Why is this aspect of Christian living so vital? _____

_____

II. PARAGRAPH DIVISIONS OF 12:1-21.

At verses 1, 3, 9.

III. ANALYSIS.

A. Introduction (12:1-2).

Read the two verses in various modern versions to feel the impact of some of the key words. For example, the phrase "be not conformed to this world" in Phillips version reads, "Don't let the world around you squeeze you into its own mold."

1. How does Paul use the phrases "of God" and "unto God"? _____

_____

What had he written about God in the verses preceding these (11:30-36)? _____

_____

2. What is meant by "present your bodies a living sacrifice"? _____

_____

_____

3. Compare the translation "reasonable service" in other versions.

4. Illustrate the difference between "conformed" and "transformed" by listing present-day practices classified under each on Chart Z.

CONFORMED—TRANSFORMED

Chart Z

Conformed to this world	Transformed

5. We all are concerned about knowing God's will for our lives. How is His will identified in verses 1-2? _____

_____

(The word "prove," v. 2, means to prove by testing, therefore "discover" or "approve.")

B. Gifts for Service (12:3-8).

1. Read the paragraph to note every reference made to the subject of gifts. Then observe the different exhortations of Paul concerning such gifts. Record these:

verse 3: _____

verses 4-5 (implied): _____

verses 6-8: _____
2. Note the variety of gifts mentioned in verses 6-8. What

is involved in each? _____

_____

Do you suppose Paul intended to include all gifts here?

_____

What is his main point? _____

_____

Compare the list of gifts in these verses with those Paul cites in I Corinthians 12:27-31 and Ephesians 4:11-12.

_____

_____

3. What important spiritual lessons are taught by this paragraph concerning the work of a local church? _____

_____

C. Obligations to Others (12:9-21).

For the remainder of the chapter Paul writes various maxims of Christian living which especially involve a Christian's relations to other people, whether they are believers or not. How do verses 9 and 21 introduce and conclude the paragraph? _____

_____

A starting point for analysis of this paragraph is to
simply list the various maxims on Chart AA. Then associate the maxims according to common subjects. (Paul
may not have intended any organized outline here as
such, but you should look for groups, for they may be
here.) Finally, apply the maxims to your own life.

MAXIMS OF 12:9-21

Verse	Maxim
10	
11	
12	
13	
14	
15-16a	
16b	
17a	
17b	
18-20	

IV. COMMENTS.

In the first verse of chapter 12 the apostle makes the
earnest appeal that we, for whom God has done so much,
shall now do something for God, namely, to present to
Him our bodies to be used in His service. In Old Testament days animals were offered to God as sacrifices. But
now we are to offer our bodies, that is, our whole beings—
body, soul, spirit.

The church, which is the body of Christ (Eph. 1:22-23),
is not an organization but an organism whose life is Christ.
Individual believers are members of this body. Each and
every member has a different gift or spiritual enablement

for service (vv. 4-5) (in this connection read I Cor. 12:4-13). These gifts should be exercised in humility, not with a view to securing praise or for gratifying vanity. We should not covet gifts which have been bestowed upon some other member, but diligently make use of the particular gift God has been pleased to grant us, for *all* gifts are important and needed (I Cor. 1' :14-22).

The basic attitude of the believer's relationship to all other people should be unfeigned love. This does not mean love only for the lovable, but love for all.

Society is made up of all kinds—Christian brethren and non-christians; some in want, others strangers; some joyful, others tearful; some whose pride prompts us to a mirroring back of the same haughtiness of spirit; some whose ill-treatment provokes to a requital in kind. All such social contacts test the Christian's temper of service.†

An abhorrence of evil is the other heart attitude spoken of by Paul in this passage. Regarding the statement in verse 17 "Recompense to no man evil for evil," someone has said:

Good for good is man-like.
Evil for evil is beast-like.
Evil for good is devil-like.
Good for evil is God-like.

V. SUMMARY.

The many commands and exhortations of Paul in chapter 12 may be grouped under three words: be, present and do.

A. Be (e.g., v. 2).
Our first concern about Christian living must be *what we are inside.* Genuine love and a hate of evil are the two primary qualities of Christian character.

B. Present (e.g., v. 1).
Christlike character demands total submission and dedication to God.

C. Do (vv. 3-21).
These commands and exhortations, though many and demanding, are a reasonable and wholesome application in daily living of the two basic commands *be* and *present.*

†Norman B. Harrison, *His Salvation*, p. 119.

The Christian Citizen

CHRISTIANS ARE NOT IN ISOLATION;

THEY ARE MEMBERS OF THEIR CHURCHES,

SOCIETIES, COUNTRIES, AND THE WORLD.

Paul has something to say in Romans 12—16 about all of these relationships. In chapter 13 he directs attention to the Christian's obligations to government and neighbors. Here is God's portrait of the genuine Christian citizen.

Since chapter 13 is a continuation of the theme begun in chapter 12, review Chart Y and study the present chapter with its surrounding context in mind.

I. PARAGRAPH DIVISIONS.

At verses 1, 8, 11.

II. ANALYSIS.

A. Subjection to Authorities (13:1-7).

Paul here clearly has in mind civil authority, though the lessons of subjection to higher authority apply to any institution.

1. In what ways are the "higher powers" described here?

_____

_____

What is meant by "ordained of God" (13:1)? _____

_____

2. Are the rulers Paul is talking about good rulers or tyrants? _____

_____

3. Who should obey governmental authority (v. 1a)?

_____

What are your reflections on the defiance of such authority
in our own land? _____

_____

Why should a Christian be a good example of a citizen?

_____

4. What is due the government by its citizens (13:7)?

_____

5. Compare these verses on the subject of authority: I
Timothy 2:1-4; I Peter 2:13-15.

B. Attitude of Love (13:8-10).
Paul cites five of the Ten Commandments, and says they
are all summed up in the one law "Thou shalt love thy
neighbor as thyself." Think about each law mentioned,
and show how fulfillment of the love law brings about
obedience to each of the other laws.

1. adultery: _____

2. killing: _____

3. stealing: _____

4. false witness: _____

5. coveting: _____

C. Armor of Light (13:11-14).
Before Paul discusses a particular problem of Christians in
chapter 14, he concludes chapters 12 and 13 with this brief
paragraph of vital exhortation. Pick out five strong phrases
in the text, and apply them to today. What is meant by

"put ye on the Lord Jesus Christ"? _____

_____

Compare this with "put on the armor of light." _____

_____

Why the picture of armor? _____

Why light? _____
Explain what Paul means by "now is our salvation nearer

than when we believed" (v. 11). _____

_____

III. COMMENTS.

A. Submission to Authority.
The Christian ought to be the very best kind of a citizen,
for real Christianity makes for good citizenship. Paul says
a Christian's proper attitude toward government is that of
submission, because civil government has its source in
God. God is the Ruler of heaven and earth. It may appear
otherwise to some, but the fact remains that "the most
High ruleth in the kingdom of men, and giveth it to whom-
soever He will" (Dan. 4:17).

God has ordained that there shall be human government
and civil laws, to preserve order. If we as Christians have
submitted ourselves wholly to God we should therefore
submit ourselves to every ordinance of God. We should
obey the laws of our land.

B. Law of Love.
The law of love is the law of Christ (cf. Gal. 6:2 with
Luke 6:27-36). Paul and John have much to say about
Christian love (read I Cor. 13:1-8; I John 4:7-12, 20-21).

Love is one debt that should always be carried—always
in the paying, yet always owing. "Pay all your debts except
the debt of love for others; never finish paying that!" (13:8,
Living Letters).

C. Armor of Light.
The last four verses of chapter 13 give a strong incentive
for the kind of living Paul has been urging upon Christians
up to this point. Regarding the statement in verse 11, "now
is our salvation nearer than when we [first] believed,"
one should remember that salvation is in three tenses: past,
present and future.

1. PAST. The believer has been saved from the guilt and penalty of sin (Luke 7:50; I Cor. 1:18; II Cor. 2:15; Eph. 2:5, 8; II Tim. 1:9).
2. PRESENT. The believer is being saved from the power of sin (Rom. 6:14; Phil. 2:12-13; Rom. 8:2; Gal. 2:19-20; II Cor. 3:18).
3. FUTURE. The believer is to be saved in the sense of entire conformity to Christ (Rom. 13:11; Heb. 10:36-37; I Peter 1:5; I John 3:2).

These three tenses of salvation might be remembered by three words, each beginning with the letter *P*. We have been saved from the *penalty* of sin; we are being saved from the *power* of sin; and there is a time coming when we shall be saved from the *presence* of sin.

IV. SUMMARY.

Respecting rulers as agents of God, and loving our neighbors as ourselves, are obligations of all Christians. The coming of the Lord draws nigh, and the temptations to consort with darkness are ever present. Paul's counsel to us is very simple though sound: "Be Christ's men from head to foot, and give no chances to the flesh to have its fling" (13:14, Phillips).

The Christian Brother

IN ANY CHRISTIAN FELLOWSHIP, THE

COMMON BOND IS THAT BELIEVERS ARE

GOD'S CHILDREN, BUT EACH DIFFERS.

There is diversity of kinds: some Christians are weak in faith, others strong; some are immature, others mature; some are carnal, others spiritual. In the passage to be studied, Paul instructs the weak and the strong how to get along with each other. The problem crops out over the question Is it right to participate in something not forbidden, as such, by Scripture?

In Paul's day, two questioned practices were (1) whether to eat all things (including meat sacrificed to idols, cf. I Cor. 8:7-13), or just vegetables; and (2) whether to esteem some holy days greater than others, or all days alike.

Today questioned practices for Christians concern such things as movies, dress and Sunday activities. The church is often torn with much bitterness, harsh criticism and misunderstanding between Christians over where the line is to be drawn concerning these. If we can identify basic *principles* of practice underlying Paul's words written almost two thousand years ago, we can apply these to today. Let this be the major task of the present study.

I. PARAGRAPH DIVISIONS.

At verses 14:1, 5, 10, 13; 15:1.

II. ANALYSIS.

After you have become acquainted with the passage through a few readings and have recorded some of your

14:1 Principle of Liberty			14:13 14:23 Principle of Love	15:1 15:7 Example of Christ
Fellowship	14:5 Service	14:10 Judgment		
"receive"	"unto the Lord"	"judgment seat"		

major impressions, begin to analyze the segment paragraph by paragraph. The accompanying outline may serve as a starter for you to see the overall plan of Paul ·in writing. Record your own observations and outlines on Chart BB.

A. Principle of Liberty (14:1-12).

The principle established here is that each Christian should *respect* the allowed liberty of the other Christian concerning a practice not expressly forbidden in Scripture (see 14:3).
Note the three paragraphs on the chart. How do the key

phrases shown represent each paragraph? _____

What are the references to the Godhead in each paragraph?° _____

_____

_____

What practical lessons are taught in these? _____

_____

_____

B. Principle of Love (14:13-23).

The timeless principle taught here is that a believer owes love to his brother, and so will not want his brother to be offended and to fall. As you study this paragraph, note the truths taught about each of the following, in their particular contexts:

death of Christ (v. 15): _____

_____

kingdom of God (v. 17): _____

_____

serving Christ (v. 18) _____

_____

edifying others (v. 19): _____

_____

What is the meaning of each of the following statements (refer to modern versions for help):

"For meat destroy not the work of God" (14:20) _____

_____

"All things indeed are pure" (14:20) _____

_____

°Note: "Judgment seat of Christ" (v. 10) reads "judgment seat of God" in the best Greek manuscripts. Here, judgment is for all. The judgment of only Christians' works is taught by II Cor. 5:10.

"Hast thou faith? Have it to thyself before God" (14:22)

Apply this paragraph to a similar present-day situation. In what ways can a strong Christian keep from casting a stumbling block in the path of a weaker brother? _____

_____

Before leaving this paragraph, bathe your heart and soul in the great love chapter of I Corinthians 13.

C. Example of Christ (15:1-7).
The example of Christ is the best instruction that can be given for dealing with problems such as chapter 14 cites. Observe the different references in this paragraph to such example. What emphasis is placed on not pleasing ourselves? _____
What is the ultimate fruit of such likemindedness (15:6-7)? _____

After you have concluded your study of this important segment, write a list of practical guides taught here concerning questioned practices. _____

_____

_____

Are you obeying the Scriptures on these points?

III. COMMENTS.

Each Christian must determine for himself, on his knees, whether it is right or wrong to engage in questioned practices. If he is *willing* to know God's mind in the matter, he will know (cf. John 7:17). If he is content only to justify a course of action he personally wants to take, or if he wants to make a display of his conscious liberty, he is off to a bad start.

According to Romans 14:1—15:7, a believer should

come to his decision of action only after he has considered his own obligations, his Christian brother's good and God's glory. Then his thinking will sound something like this: "This thing seems perfectly right to me. I can do it with a clear conscience so far as I myself am concerned, but when others are led into sin by my self-indulgence it grieves God and hinders His work. I love my God and do not want to grieve Him or hinder His work. On the contrary I want to glorify Him before men. I want to live a Christlike life, and even Christ pleased not Himself. Therefore, for the glory of God I will refrain from doing this thing."

*　　*　　*

IV. CONCLUSION (15:8-13).

These verses, which include a benediction (15:13), conclude the main body of Paul's epistle, for beginning at 15:14 Paul makes personal notations concerning himself and the people to whom he writes the letter.
Read verses 8-12 and note references to Jew and Gentile. Recall what Paul has written about both groups throughout the epistle. What does he say about Christ's ministry

to the Jews? _____

_____

What is the atmosphere of these verses? _____

_____

How are they a fitting conclusion to the doctrinal and

practical divisions of the epistle? _____

_____

Study the benediction phrase by phrase, and show how it

also is an appropriate conclusion. _____

_____

_____

_____

_____

Epilogue: Personal Notes

THE WRITER'S PERSONAL REMARKS IN
CLOSING HIS LETTERS ARE INTERESTING
AND REVEALING PARTS OF SCRIPTURE.

Tarry long over this passage, for it will encourage your own heart to know that Christians in Paul's day, including Paul himself, were real people and human. Paul, inspired of the Holy Spirit, wrote as one who knew by experience of that which he wrote.

This epilogue may be divided into two parts for study:

Paul's Testimony and Plans (15:14-33)
Paul's Friends and Co-workers (16:1-27)

I. PARAGRAPH DIVISIONS.

At verses 15:14, 22, 30; 16:1, 3, 17, 21, 25.

II. ANALYSIS.

A. Paul's Testimony and Plans (15:14-33).

Record below what these verses reveal about:

1. Paul's character: _____

_____

_____

_____

_____

2. Paul's ministry: _____

_____
_____
_____
_____

3. Paul's plans: _____

_____
_____
_____
_____

4. Paul's requests: _____

_____
_____
_____
_____

B. Paul's Friends and Co-Workers (16:1-27).

The prominent feature of this chapter is the multitude of names cited by Paul. Some of those mentioned are Jews, some Gentiles. Some are men, some women. Some are in secular work (e.g., tent-making), some in the gospel ministry. What does a name represent? _____

_____

What spiritual lesson is suggested by the fact that names of even common people find a place in this book of God?

_____

Go through the chapter and note especially the descriptions Paul gives to many of these friends and co-workers. Write out the list on paper, and derive some lessons from this. Read the list of names and deeds of David's mighty men recorded in II Samuel 23:8-39.

Paul cites a problem in verses 17-18. How does he refer to it in verses 19-20a? _____

_____

Note the benedictions of verses 20b and 24.* Compare these with 15:13, 33. Then study carefully the doxology of 16:25-27. How does it reflect some of the major doctrines which Paul has taught in the epistle? _____

_____

Note the concluding reference to the glory of God. Compare this with the references to glory in the concluding paragraph of 15:8-13.

III. A FINAL THOUGHT.

Throughout his letter to the Romans Paul has set forth the *true* doctrines of the gospel of God. Now, in a brief paragraph contained in this last chapter, he gives a solemn warning regarding false doctrine, taught by those who "by good words and fair speeches deceive the hearts of the simple" (16:18).

If one is grounded in the truths set forth in the book of Romans it will be easy to "mark" the false teachers. False teachers are those whose teachings contradict the truths of the gospel of God. That gospel, so fully presented in Romans, includes such doctrines as

the exceeding sinfulness of sin
the utterly lost and helpless condition of the unregenerate
the grace of the almighty, sovereign God
faith in the substitutionary death of Christ as the only way of salvation;
the power of the indwelling Holy Spirit for Christian living

Acquaintance with the message and methods of false teachers is helpful to the Christian to avoid the pitfalls of false doctrine, but the basic antidote is a knowledge of the true doctrines of the Bible. The Spirit of God gave

*Verse 24 is not found in some of the better Greek manuscripts.

to the world the epistle to the Romans to set forth loudly and clearly the true gospel of God's salvation. It has been our privilege to study the great themes of this gospel as presented in this rich epistle through the pen of Paul.

Found on Flyleaf of Moody's Bible

Repentance—a change of mind;
  New mind about GOD.
Conversion—a change of life;
  New life for GOD.
Regeneration—a change of nature;
  New heart for GOD.
Justification—a change of state;
  New standing for GOD.
Adoption—a change of family:
  New relationship toward GOD.
Sanctification—a change of service;
  Separation unto GOD.
Glorification—a change of place;
  New condition with GOD.

Moody Press, a ministry of the Moody Bible Institute, is designed for education, evangelization and edification. If we may assist you in knowing more about Christ and the Christian life, please write us without obligation to: Moody Press, c/o MLM, Chicago, Illinois 60610.

Bibliography

Bruce, F. F. *The Letters of Paul*. Grand Rapids: Eerdmans, 1965.

Erdman, Charles R. *The Epistle of Paul to the Romans*. Philadelphia: Westminster, 1942.

The Four Translation New Testament. Chicago: Moody, 1966.

Godet, F. *Commentary on St. Paul's Epistle to the Romans*. Trans. A. Cusin. New York: Funk & Wagnalls, 1883.

Hamilton, Floyd E. *The Epistle to the Romans*. Grand Rapids: Baker, 1958.

Harrison, Norman B. *His Salvation*. Minneapolis: Harrison, 1924.

Hiebert, D. Edmond. *An Introduction to the Pauline Epistles*. Chicago: Moody, 1954.

Hodge, Charles. *Commentary on the Epistle to the Romans*. New ed.; New York: Armstrong, 1890.

Lenski, R. C. H. *The Interpretation of St. Paul's Epistle to the Romans*. Columbus, Ohio: Wartburg, 1945.

McQuilkin, Robert C. *The Message of Romans*. Grand Rapids: Zondervan, 1947.

Moule, Handley C. G. *The Epistle of Paul to the Romans*. *The Expositor's Bible*. New York: Armstrong, 1894.

Murray, John. *The Epistle to the Romans*. Vols. I and II. Grand Rapids: Eerdmans, 1959, 1965.

Newell, William R. *Romans Verse by Verse*. Chicago: Moody, 1948.

Pfeiffer, Charles F., and Harrison, Everett F. *The Wycliffe Bible Commentary*. Chicago: Moody, 1963.

Schaff, Philip. *History of the Christian Church*. Vol. I. New York: Scribner, 1895.

Shedd, William G. T. *A Critical and Doctrinal Commentary upon the Epistle of St. Paul to the Romans*. Grand Rapids: Zondervan, 1967. Reprint of 1879 edition.

Thomas, W. H. Griffith. *Romans I—XVI: A Devotional Commentary*. Grand Rapids: Eerdmans, 1953.

Unger, Merrill F. *Unger's Bible Handbook*. Chicago: Moody, 1966.

Wuest, Kenneth S. *Romans in the Greek New Testament*. Grand Rapids: Eerdmans, 1955.

NOTES

NOTES

NOTES